SOCIAL SETTINGS
AND
MEDICAL
ORGANIZATION

The Author

WILLIAM A. GLASER is Senior Research Associate in the Bureau of Applied Social Research at Columbia University. At present he is Director of the Bureau's Program of International and Comparative Research. He received his B.A. from New York University and his M.A. and Ph.D. from Harvard University. Dr. Glaser has conducted extensive research in medical care, comparative social structure, and U.S. government and elections. He has written and edited several books, including a comparative study of physicians' remuneration, *Paying the Doctor* (1970).

A PROJECT OF THE
BUREAU OF
APPLIED SOCIAL RESEARCH
COLUMBIA UNIVERSITY

William A. Glaser

SOCIAL SETTINGS
AND
MEDICAL
ORGANIZATION
A Cross-National
Study of the Hospital

ATHERTON PRESS, INC. · New York · 1970

Library of Congress Catalog Card Number 74–92061

FIRST EDITION

Manufactured in the United States of America

Designed by CAROLE HALPERT

for Todd

Acknowledgments

For helpful comments on various drafts of this book, I am indebted to Robert K. Merton, Philip Kronenberg, Juan Linz, Charles Kadushin, Samuel Z. Klausner, Herbert Menzel, Sydney Spivack, James Price, Carl E. Taylor, Keith O. Taylor, Gertrude A. Ramsden, Sister Anthony Marie, and Eugenia K. Spalding. Hans Zetterberg and Yvonne Schroeder Jayawardena provided advice on the basis of the planning papers that preceded the field research.

The gathering of data overseas and the preparation of this manuscript were made possible by grants RG-7934, CH-00027, and CH-00298 of the National Institutes of Health, United States Public Health Service. Initial planning was supported by a residency awarded by the Russell Sage Foundation.

The study was administered at the Bureau of Applied Social Research by Clara Shapiro and Madeline Simonson. The manuscript was typed by Nelson Glover.

I am most indebted to the many medical administrators and scholars abroad who were so generous with their time and information. The numerous persons who granted me interviews and allowed me to visit their organizations are listed in the Appendix.

Contents

SOCIAL SETTINGS
AND
MEDICAL
ORGANIZATION

1
Comparative Perspectives on Hospitals

Every social system must cope with several problems arising out of the physical and mental illnesses of its members. Cures must be effected; because ill persons are exempted from their usual social roles, the successful functioning of all other social institutions requires a sufficient number of cures within a short time. The population must be taught to avoid accidents and illnesses. The social system's survival requires a sufficient reproduction of its population, and widespread illness diminishes reproduction. If the terminally ill are cared for rather than neglected or destroyed, suitable staff and facilities must be procured and organized. Illness and death arouse anxiety in the population—particularly among the afflicted—and cognitive explanations and rituals are provided. Certain procedures must be performed if the culture specifies that souls and corpses should reach certain goals.

These aims may be accomplished by a loose division of labor in the larger society. Certain groups (such as the family) may perform several custodial and therapeutic tasks along with their many other tasks. Other groups (such as the churches) supply the explanations and ceremonies.

This type of functionally diffuse social system eventually is superseded by a more specialized division of labor. New classes of organizations—like hospitals—are created to perform tasks more efficiently than was possible in the multifunctional groups initially created primarily for other purposes. If an organization's structure and procurement policies are devoted to fulfillment of a particular goal, success will likely be greater. For example, scientific medical care probably will be performed more efficiently by a hospital specializing in such work, than by a family pursuing numerous and varied ends. Another reason for creation of specialized organizations is innovation: the newest methods often are not readily adopted by established organizations with customary structures and procurement practices.

Every organization may be conceived as a system of production. Personnel are arranged to accomplish common goals by means of a particular technology. When examining any organization, the starting points are its intended output, its technological means to produce the results, the technically determined organization of relations among people to accomplish the results, and the nontechnically determined relations among people within the organization.[1]

Hospitals interest sociologists because they vary so widely. In defining who is sick, who needs treatment, and what treatments are best, hospitals throughout history and in the present day pursue a great variety of goals. The technology of medical care has changed greatly and still ranges widely today in the world, and therefore hospitals vary considerably in their technology. Even when their goals and techniques are similar, hospital managements may organize work quite differently. Hospitals are found in diverse social settings; they may articulate with other groups and organizations in varied ways even in comparable social environments; and therefore additional sources of variation in hospital social structure are generated.

How different social settings produce different organizational forms is the central theme of this book. Every class of organizations is particularly dependent on certain institutional spheres for inputs of personnel, resources, and information governing its structure and performance. Every class of organizations is intimately articulated with particular institutional spheres that depend for their own success on the fulfillment of those organizations' goals. Because hospitals mobilize people, objects, and technical knowledge to care for and restore persons, they depend on religious, economic, and educational institutions. Because they are an alternative to the family in the care of sick members and because they rely so heavily on female employees, they are powerfully affected by the society's family institutions. Families and economic organizations in turn depend on hospitals for successful treatment of their members and for satisfactory management of incurables. Churches too are interested in the performance of hospitals, because certain medical and housekeeping activities may bear upon the churches' values and because some religious personnel may gain vocational rewards from service in the hospitals.

Comparative Organizational Sociology

Sociology searches for patterns in human life. Such statements, however, are usually conditional rather than universal. A particular relationship may occur in certain social contexts but not in others. Therefore, the same type of group, organization, or relationship should be observed in many different social systems before one can be sure how it originates, how it evolves, and how it is connected with other variables in larger social settings.

For many years the literature of organizational sociology was full of universal generalizations, when the data had come from only one country, usually the United States. But the sociologically sensitive traveler can see that the particular type of organization is somewhat different in structure, performance, and goals in another country. That an organizational form cannot easily be exported to another society without adaptation has become evident to industrial executives, educational administrators, management experts, and others trying to create international networks, or trying to build newly developing countries. Therefore, the task in both sociological theory and social practice is to identify the connections between the elements of an organization and the social institutions, groups, and other organizations that supply its inputs and use its outputs.

Systematic comparisons require arranging social systems along scales. If the problem is to identify the effects of different types of society on organizations, a theoretical typology or continuum of social systems is developed, measures of actual social systems according to the theoretical continuum are gathered, the societies are then classified along the typology or scale, differences are identified in characteristics of certain comparable formal organizations, and explanations of the observed differences in organizational structure and function are sought in the interactions between the organizations and their parent social systems.

Another strategy in making cross-national comparisons is to correlate the structural characteristics of the larger society and of comparable organizations. The social system is not examined and classified as a unit, but particular variables are abstracted and related. For example, cross-national comparisons of this type are addressed to discovering whether greater egalitarianism in family institutions ccrrelates with greater egalitarianism in the authority structure of the factory; whether rising national income correlates with more or less conflict among ranks within bureaucracies; whether a higher rate of communications within a society produces greater division of labor and specificity of function within organizations.[2]

Comparisons of institutional characteristics and their effects can be cross-sectional: societies are compared at the point of time when the data are gathered. One can also compare the same society at different times. when many of its institutional characteristics have changed. Changes in certain determinants, such as family structure, are then related to changes in dependent variables, such as the typical authority structures of factories. Many comparisons among societies presume that social structures are much alike, and that cross-national differences in data really record stages that many social systems will experience at some time. Comparisons of underdeveloped and developed societies often assume that many institutions in the former are evolving into patterns much like the latter's. Therefore, for example, a hypothesis correlating the structural differentiation of a society with the rate of elite mobility must satisfy two empirical tests: among contemporaneous societies, the more differentiated should have more mobility among elites; in each society at successive times, increasing structural differentiation should bring about greater elite mobility.[3]

Theoretically important and empirically valid comparisons of social systems are far more difficult to make than comparisons of correlations among a few variables abstracted from several societies. Consequently the research literature in comparative sociology consists almost entirely of the latter type of work.

Comparative Analysis of Hospitals

Hospitals are strategic subjects for making cross-national comparisons of organizational life, since they are sensitive to variations in
surrounding social institutions. This book will focus on the relations between the hospital and the religious, family, and economic
institutions, because of their special interconnection in both inputs
and outputs. For simplicity, separate chapters will describe some
effects upon the hospital of cross-national variations in each institutional sector. (Because religion, family, and economy interact
and produce joint inputs, the following chapters will not always
follow the division rigorously but will frequently mention joint
effects.[4])

Other strategies can be used for comparing societies and their
constituent organizations.[5] The method I have adopted derives
from the conception of macrosociology as the study of relationships between different institutional spheres. Therefore each chapter relates the hospital to determinants among nonmedical
institutions.[6] This book examines the effects of selected nonmedical
institutions; I have published elsewhere more complete details
about how hospitals compare in different countries, because of
administrative customs or because of variations in medical practice.[7]

Each chapter presents considerable detail about how religion,
the family, and the economy affect hospitals. In completely new
fields, such as cross-national research about organizations, bare
propositions seem unreal and suspect unless the reader can get the
"feel" of the evidence supporting them. But the goal of social
science is systems of propositions about structures and processes.
Therefore each chapter concludes with a list of tentative propositions about nonmedical social structures and hospital structures
that seem supported by the evidence available. The final chapter
summarizes some relationships between changes in the nonmedical
social structures and changes in hospital organizations.

A goal of science is parsimony: each investigatiion should test
a system of propositions based on a minimum number of variables,
stated abstractly in order to encompass the maximum range of
data. But this is possible only after collection of a great deal of

evidence and only after much low-level theorizing. Because comparative organizational sociology has begun to develop only recently and has not yet progressed far beyond factual reports, a sufficient body of verified propositions for replication in research about hospitals is not available.[8] And because virtually no sociological facts about hospitals in different countries have yet been published, this book has to perform the double function of introducing comparative empirical reporting about hospitals as well as sketching some theoretical strategies in proposition-building. Consequently, the variables and propositions at the end of each chapter are more numerous and are stated in more common-sense language than will be used after more research in comparative organizational sociology. At times I include in the factual presentations data that might interest the reader but that cannot easily be apprehended by the propositions at the end of this chapter. However, the text does revolve around certain main themes. Although the chapters attempt to isolate the independent effects of religion, the family, and the economy, the same areas of hospital organization recur. In other words, most of the dependent variables—and therefore most of the factual text—concern goals, the recruitment of clients and working personnel, the skills and motivations of personnel, and authority inside the organization.[9]

The discussion concerns only general hospitals. Societal influences relate to specialized hospitals somewhat differently, and the text would be complicated excessively by including them.

Research Methods

This book is based on interviews, observations, and a review of pertinent literature. From May 1961 through August 1962 I visited the following countries and interviewed informants about medical organization: England, Sweden, the Netherlands, West Germany, France, Switzerland, Spain, Italy, Greece, Poland, the Soviet Union, Turkey, Cyprus, Lebanon, Egypt, and Israel. Those countries were selected that would provide a sufficient range on the institutional variables I had previously picked for this book. I sought to travel to as many and as varied a set of countries as possible within the limits of budget and time. In 1966, I revisited several informants in The Netherlands, West Germany, and France. Besides visits to individual countries, I also interviewed informants at the World Health Organization's main headquarters, its European Regional Office, and its Eastern Mediterranean Regional Office.

Interviews lasted from a few minutes to ten or more hours. Informants in each country were as numerous and drawn from as varied a background as could be sampled during a limited time. In each country I talked to those people who could provide accurate information about the topics being studied, usually including the following: the chief nurse, the international relations officer, the chief medical officer, and other officials of the Ministry of Health; the chief medical officer and other officials of the national office of the health insurance system; secretaries and presidents of the medical, nursing, and hospital associations; some professors in medical and nursing schools; lay administrators, medical directors, and matrons of some hospitals; young house officers and undergraduate medical students; private medical practitioners; and scholars who have done research on medical organization. Attempts were always made to interview the opposite sides of controversial relations, such as both the administrators of the sick funds and the secretary of the medical association. members of different groups in ethnically divided countries, proponents of reform and of the *status quo*. Interviews with WHO officials concerned primarily African or Asian countries that they had visited; some of the informants were then long-term consultants in such countries, and they were interviewed during their annual visits to headquarters. (A partial list of the informants is in the appendix.) Most interviews were conducted in English or in French; for a few interviews in the Soviet Union and in Germany, interpreters were used. Usually I was alone with the informant.

Besides interviewing, I visited many hospitals, polyclinics, medical schools, nursing schools, and other installations to learn how they were organized and operated. In each country I saw between two and ten hospitals, during what were often all-day visits combining tours through the buildings, long interviews with the administrators, brief informal chats with doctors and nurses in the wards, and observations of operating theater teams at work. I sought out the less publicized and more typical installations in both the capital city and in distant areas. For example, I visited hospitals and clinics in Nardokallix, Sweden; Klirou, Cyprus; Tanta, Egypt; Lormes, France; Lietkin, the U.S.S.R.; and Afula, Israel.

Sometimes I watched people at work. The informants often interrupted our interviews to transact their customary administrative work in their native languages. In a few countries I attended meetings of committees that managed hospitals and other organizations. Sometimes I followed medical school professors on their teaching rounds.

Besides interviews and observations, this book is based on a sampling of the literature, performed during a one-year preparation before I went overseas and supplemented by library research at the World Health Organization's Geneva office, in London, and in New York after my return. This can be no more than a sampling, since the amount of literature on medical organization is enormous. Many books describe health institutions in different countries. Medical, nursing, hospital, and social science journals are full of descriptions of one's own country and provide some suggestive travelers' impressions of other countries. I collected many annual reports and memoranda from such sources as Ministries of Health, sick funds, and hospitals. In some reference libraries and in some government offices I was allowed to see normally restricted information, such as consultants' reports evaluating the performance of a country's medical services, and communications between the Ministries of Health and Finance.[10]

Ideally, cross-national comparisons of hospitals and of their macrosociological determinants should be based on harder data than informant interviews, observations, case reports, and similar miscellaneous evidence. The modal characteristics of each country should be calculated on the basis of extensive research about hospitals, religion, the family, and the economy; then countries should be compared along an array; and only then can a proposition be asserted.

But it is not yet possible to make systematic comparisons involving many countries with complete and reliable statistical indicators about the relevant social institutions and the characteristics of hospital organizations. Good statistics exist in many countries about some social institutions supplying inputs to hospitals (notably the economy, education, and government), but statistics are too sparse for good cross-national comparisons in other institutional spheres that are crucial for hospitals (such as religion and the family). A serious handicap now is the paucity of adequate statistics for secondary analysis of a sociological sort about the goals, structure, and performance of hospitals themselves.[11] Research possibilities will improve in the future. An increasing number of countries have good data about the physical condition of the population;[12] some developed countries have conducted national surveys of the utilization of medical services by the population;[13] and comparable statistics are now being gathered for the first time about hospital administration.[14]

Constructing Empirical Propositions

A verbal manuscript can summarize relationships among the variables that constitute a social system, but it cannot easily summarize the social system itself. The human mind can apprehend and describe the interactions among only a few variables, but special aids to theory and to presentation are needed when the few variables have feedback and other loops, and when the system contains more than a small number of variables.[15] These nonverbal aids include mathematical models or computer simulation programs, whose parameters and whose interrelations correspond to the events discovered in empirical research.

The chapter summaries will list relationships between nonmedical social institutions and hospital organizations, abstracted from the details presented in the text. The summaries list the principal propositions most strongly supported by my evidence, but the text presents considerable detail suggesting other relationships as well. The propositions concluding each chapter can become parts of comprehensive theories about the mutual effects between hospital organizations and their social settings.[16] No more than a few propositions would be combined in any theory. Ideally, the fewest possible variables should generate the largest number of propositions that are highly general and also are not trite.

Following is a list of variables pertaining to hospital organization and discussed in this book. Other significant variables concerning the inputs, structure, performance, and outputs of hospital organizations might be added, but I lacked enough evidence about their relations with other social institutions to give them prominence in this book. For simplicity in this introductory study, I shall list two-variable propositions; but many multivariate and conditional propositions also could be constructed from my basic list of macrosociological independent variables and organizational dependent variables. Since they will recur in the summaries of Chapters 2–4, the organizational variables are numbered for convenience in cross-referencing and for identifying the elements in the propositions that will follow. The variables pertaining to hospital organizations are designated entirely by Arabic numerals. The determining variables from nonmedical institutions—to be listed as parts of the propositions themselves—will be identified by numbers prefixed by letters.[17]

1.0 Inputs into hospitals
    1.1 Recruitment of employees
        1.1.1 Number
        1.1.2 Skills
        1.1.3 Sex
        1.1.4 Attitudes
    1.2 Investment of buildings
    1.3 Investment of technology
        1.3.1 Amount
        1.3.2 Complexity
    1.4 Utilization of ambulatory services
        1.4.1 Sex
        1.4.2 Class
    1.5 Utilization of inpatient services
        1.5.1 Sex
        1.5.2 Class
    1.6 Time of referral
    1.7 Regional distribution
2.0 Organization of the individual hospital
    2.1 Size
    2.2 Number of departments
    2.3 Numbers of personnel
        2.3.1 Doctors
        2.3.2 Graduate nurses
        2.3.3 Auxiliaries

Notes

1. Such a conception of organizations is summarized and applied to hospitals in Charles Perrow, "Hospitals: Technology, Structure, and Goals," in James G. March (ed.), *Handbook of Organizations* (Chicago: Rand McNally, 1965), pp. 913–916. The rest of Perrow's article is a valuable summary of the American literature about the social structure of hospitals.

2. Many of these studies are summarized in Robert M. Marsh, *Comparative Sociology* (New York: Harcourt, Brace & World, 1967).

3. Many evolutionary studies are summarized in *ibid.*

4. Governmental and educational institutions also affect hospital organization. But here I consider them transmitters of influences ultimately originating in the spheres of religion, family, and economy.

5. The various ways of conducting comparative research and reporting the results are described in Terence K. Hopkins and Immanuel Wallerstein, "The Comparative Study of National Societies," *Social Science Information*, 6:5 (October 1967), 27–33.

6. This approach is described more generally in Samuel Z. Klausner (ed.), *The Study of Total Societies* (Garden City, N.Y.: Doubleday, 1967), pp. 3–29. I use similar reasoning in making cross-national comparisons of the social structure of factories in other research now under way.

7. See my articles, "American and Foreign Hospitals: Some Sociological Comparisons," in Eliot Freidson (ed.), *The Hospital in Modern Society* (New York: The Free Press, 1963), Ch. 2; "The Problems of the Hospital Administrator: Some American and Foreign Comparisons," *Hospital Administration*, 9:3 (Summer 1964), 6–22; and "Nursing Leadership and Policy: Some Cross-National Comparisons, " in Fred Davis (ed.), *The Nursing Profession* (New York: Wiley, 1966), pp. 1–59. Administrative details about hospitals in individual countries appear in several treatises, such as Malcolm T. MacEachern, *Hospital Organization and Management* (Chicago: Physicians' Record Company, 3rd ed., 1957); J. E. Stone, *Hospital Organisation and Management* (London: Faber and Faber, 4th ed., 1952); Henri Thoillier, *L'Hôpital Français* (Paris: Techniques Hospitalières, 2nd ed., 1947); Robert F. Bridgman, *L'Hôpital et la Cité* (Paris: Editions du Cosmos, 1961); Maria Gehrt and Karl Heinz Stiefel, *Das Krankenhausarchiv* (Cologne: Kohlhammer Verlag, 1963); and B. Moretti, *Ospedali* (Milan: U. Hoepli, 3rd ed., 1951).

8. Enough sociological research has been done about industry and work throughout the world that propositional theorizing has begun with these data. For example, the concept of "labor commitment" is used as the organizing theme for a summary of the knowledge about industrialization in Wilbert E. Moore and Arnold S. Feld-

man (eds.), *Labor Commitment and Social Change in Developing Areas* (New York: Social Science Research Council, 1960). A propositional inventory about the organization of work and macrosociological correlates in preindustrial societies appears in Stanley Udy, *Organization of Work* (New Haven: HRAF Press, 1959).

9. The value of exploratory studies at this stage of comparative organizational sociology is stated by Stanley Udy, "The Comparative Analysis of Organizations," in March, *Handbook of Organizations*, pp. 683–687. Ultimately, comparative organizational sociology requires counts of organizational types in numerous social systems. This point is made by Arthur L. Stinchcombe in his very valuable article summarizing existing knowledge about the relations between social environments and organizations, "Social Structure and Organizations," in March, *Handbook*, at p. 153. Parenthetically, another handicap at present in arranging a manuscript comparing organizations in different societies is the shortage of systematic, empirically verified theories about organizations. Rather, the literature presents many conceptual schemes dependent on authors' personal tastes, and it presents many empirical findings. Some lists of discrete empirical findings have been published, but most are not addressed to our problem of relating a range of organizations and their social environments. The limitations of the organizational literature are well stated by W. Richard Scott, "Theory of Organizations," in Robert E. L. Faris (ed.), *Handbook of Modern Sociology* (Chicago: Rand McNally, 1964), p. 485. Scott (at p. 520) notes the paucity of research and commentary about relationships between organizations and their environments.

10. The publications about underdeveloped countries cited in these notes refer disproportionately to Africa and India. The reason is that Englishmen and former English subjects are most interested in writing about medical organization and medically relevant behavior. My generalizations are not based on anglophone Africa and India alone but encompass informant interviews, unpublished reports, and personal observations about many countries.

11. Statistics about certain sociologically important aspects of hospitals are not yet gathered in many countries. Of the published data, many are unreliable. Some of the defects are mentioned in *Survey of Social Statistics* (New York: United Nations, 1954), pp. 19–22, and Robert F. L. Logan and T. S. Eimerl, "Case Loads in Hospitals and General Practice in Several Countries," in Roy M. Acheson (ed.), *Comparability in International Epidemiology* (New York: The Milbank Memorial Fund, 1965), pp. 302–304. The hazards of secondary analysis with national statistics are summarized in Oskar Morgenstern, *The Accuracy of Economic Observations* (Princeton, N.J.: Princeton University Press, 2nd ed., 1963); Donald V. McGranahan, "Comparative Social Research in the United Nations," in Richard L. Merritt and Stein Rokkan (eds.), *Comparing Nations* (New Haven: Yale University Press, 1966), pp. 528–529, 536–537, etc. passim; and "What Indicates What?" *The American Behavioral Scientist*, 8:4 (December 1964), 29–31.

12. The state of epidemiological statistics for purposes of cross-national comparisons is described by Fraser Brockington, *World Health* (Harmondsworth: Penguin Books, 1958), Part 6; and Satya Swaroop, "Study of Morbidity in Underdeveloped Areas," *International Population Conference*, Vienna, 1959, pp. 543–553.

13. A few studies now are designed to produce valid cross-national comparisons, e.g., Kerr L. White et al., "International Comparisons of Medical-Care Utilization," *The New England Journal of Medicine*, 217 (7 September 1967), 516–522; and Osler L. Peterson et al., "What Is Value for Money in Medical Care? Experiences in England and Wales, Sweden, and the U.S.A.," *The Lancet*, 8 (April 1967), 771–776.

14. Simon Btesh, "International Research in the Organization of Medical Care," *Medical Care*, 3:1 (January–March 1965), 41–46; and Robert F. Bridgman, "An International Study on Hospital Utilization" (Geneva: World Health Organization, 1967, mimeographed). The new methods of surveying large samples of each country's organizations are described in Wolf V. Heydebrand, "The Study of Organizations," *Social Science Information*, 7:5 (October 1967), 65–81. Heydebrand reports such a national survey of American hospitals in his *Hospital Bureaucracy* (Chicago: The University of Chicago Press, 1969).

15. On the difficulty of thinking about dynamic systems and on the need for mathematical or computer models as statements of systems theories, see Jay W. Forrester, *Industrial Dynamics* (Cambridge: The M.I.T. Press, 1961), p. 99. Strategies for theorizing about social systems by means of computer simulation are summarized by Ithiel de Sola Pool, "Computer Simulations of Total Societies," in Samuel Z. Klausner (ed.), *The Study of Total Societies* (Garden City, N.Y.: Doubleday, 1967), pp. 45–65. On the method of constructing the basic theoretical models about social systems, see Everett E. Hagen, "Analytical Models in the Study of Social Systems," *The American Journal of Sociology*, 67:2 (September 1961), 144–151.

16. In earlier research, several colleagues and I attempted to develop theories about the electoral system in the United States. A few chapters in that book listed propositions that would be combined in systems theories, like the lists of propositions concluding each chapter in this volume. Other chapters in the earlier book summarized comprehensive theories about the electoral system based on computer simulation and on econometric reasoning. William N. McPhee and William A. Glaser (eds.), *Public Opinion and Congressional Elections* (New York: The Free Press, 1962).

17. A similar—but not identical—method of coding variables and stating propositions appears throughout James G. March and Herbert A. Simon, *Organizations* (New York: Wiley, 1958).

2

Religion

A society's assumptions about causes of diseases are the strongest and most immediate correlates of the goals, techniques, and personal organization of its hospitals. Every organization may be conceived as an institutionalization of a prevailing belief system in that field. Obviously, a society's prevailing theories about the causes of disease will determine whether patients seek practical remedies, the stage of the illness when they act, where they seek assistance, their behavior during therapy, and their expectations about outcomes. Ideas about the causes of disease can be classified as follows:

1. Coercive intrusion into the organism of evil spirits, ideas, foreign objects, bacteria, or viruses.
2. Deficient, excessive, or faulty intake of food, fluid, gases, poisons, or information.
3. Deficient, excessive, or faulty output as it occurs in disordered elimination, excessive work and strain, inability to express feelings and thoughts, atrophy or hypertrophy of certain physical structures, or one-sided development of social and psychological functions.
4. Loss of or deficiency in essential parts; e.g., mental deficiency, castration, abortion, sensory defects, mutilation, loss of love objects, or loss of hope.
5. Disintegration of orderly structures as in cancer, toxic states, and senile psychoses, or breakdown of social relations and patterns of communication.[1]

Theories of disease contrast by attributing each illness to different individual physical events or combination of events. Further, they differ in their chains of causality: some theories postulate a series of physical and supernatural events ultimately controlled by a supernatural force; other theories confine explanations to a few mundane variables. Associated with these causal theories are ideas about prevention and remedies: whether action is worthwhile depends on whether the disease is reversible and whether further problems are preventable; the specific place and nature of the action will depend on the particular cause to be manipulated; and the character of the action will depend on whether a permanent or temporary solution is sought. Theories of disease will govern not only the search for help by afflicted persons but also the procurement and performance of therapeutic personnel and facilities.[2]

As this book will demonstrate, some theories of disease are compatible with various types of hospital organization, while other theories are inimical toward all or some types. The Western hospital depends on certain assumptions about the causes and manipulation of disease. In many societies the entire population behaves according to these beliefs, but elsewhere substantial numbers of patients and of hospital employees act according to other theories of disease. Therefore one encounters not only cross-national differences in type of hospital but also differences in how the Western type of hospital functions in practice.

A simple theory about the ultimate determinants of types of hospital in different countries could derive from classifications of societies' different notions about the causes of disease. But such correlations are high because they are tautological: both a population's predominant etiological beliefs and its typical therapeutic facilities are closely connected parts of its system of medical institutions, and the theories of disease are both the motivations and an ideological output of the facilities. For example, obviously theories that disease is entirely somatic and reversible by physical manipulation of the patient is associated with a hospital system quite different from the organizational correlates of theories attributing disease to supernatural vengeance. Comparative sociology searches for determinants in other institutional spheres. Theories of disease will enter our analysis often as intervening variables that derive from various religions, economic conditions, or educational settings. As we shall see, the etiological implications of each religion have crucial effects upon the behavior of patients and employees both in indigenously originated hospitals and in installations imported from the West.

Religious Inputs into Hospitals

Both religion and medicine provide explanations and offer remedies to persons experiencing suffering. Both prescribe from bodies of theory about physical events that provoke anxiety. Both expect the individual and his relatives to adopt certain beliefs and perform particular actions in order to reduce suffering. Therefore hospitals are heavily affected by religions, and the modernization of hospitals may produce conflicts with churches and their communicants.

A religion will affect hospitals because of its doctrines. Its explanation of physical events may inform the sufferer and hospital personnel about the causes of the affliction and the most appropriate actions. The religion's doctrines may motivate persons to become patients: its conceptions of the avoidability and undesirability of physical suffering balanced against the results and desirability of death will affect the urgency for seeking medical solutions. Doctrines about the way to secure salvation and about the proper relationships among people will affect recruitment into hospital work and will affect how such employees treat patients and the public.

The organization of a religion will affect hospitals. Some churches have programs of charity and social welfare in order to serve doctrinal principle or missionary tactic. Some have means for raising funds, recruiting and administering appropriate personnel for hospital work, and managing complex organizations of a lay character.

Some religions affect hospitals by creating a need for them. The membership may tend to concentrate together in urban conditions, thus creating a need for mass therapeutic centers. Certain doctrines may stimulate pilgrimages and other movements, thereby increasing contagions and physical stresses, and thus creating a need for some alternative to family care. The church may employ or protect many persons and thus assume the responsibility for housing and treating them. Some religious doctrines may prescribe surgical or medical rituals that can be done most safely in a medical setting.

Religious Origins of the Modern Hospital

Before hospitals can arise, a particular combination of inputs must be available from the social system. Money and materials are needed for buildings; personnel and managerial skills must be forthcoming; therapeutic methods must require inpatient care; patients must have certain clinical conditions, motivations to submit to hospitalization, and capacity to play patient roles. Certain combinations of inputs will result in the absence of hospitals; other combinations lead to the creation of hospitals with various goals and organization structures. Certain combinations of inputs produce special adaptation problems when Western hospitals are imported into a different kind of society.

Judaism. The modern hospital sprang from the religious tradition initiated by ancient Judaism and continued by Islam and Christianity. As we shall see, the full set of necessary ideas and institutional conditions was present in medieval and postmedieval Christianity, so that the contemporary hospital is a secularized modern version of the earlier Christian hospital.

Many religions and cultures have taught the duty of the family to care for its sick members. Many societies have maintained a few buildings for the custody of injured soldiers or for sick people whose maladies are considered a public threat. For example, compulsory isolation of lepers in special establishments has been widespread and is mentioned as early as the Old Testament.[3] But these scattered facilities are not the same as a nationwide system of hospitals, staffed by specialists obliged to provide treatment and housing for any person who seeks entry.

One of the fundamental presuppositions of the modern hospital is that one person should devote labor and resources to the physical cure and housing of a sick stranger, a principle critically different from mutual obligations within the family. Ancient Judaism is a religion of commandments from God, with warnings about divine wrath for disobedience. Among the commandments are to "love ye therefore the stranger"[4] and give charity to the poor and needy.[5] Possessors of worldly goods got them from God and are simply acting as His obedient agents in distributing them according to His will. Consequently, the charitable are righteous and will be rewarded both in this world and the next; any who ignore the needy shall be punished by God.[6] Besides individual alms, the Hebrews developed organized charity by communal agencies.[7] Visiting and caring for the sick are not specifically mentioned in the Old Testament, but the Rabbis in the Talmud include this by deduction among the charitable duties incumbent upon every Jew.[8]

Because illness is an uncomfortable and apparently mysterious event that evokes anxiety and premonitions about death, every religion provides doctrinal explanations of its causes and at least some hints about appropriate action. Like many other religions, ancient Judaism interpreted illness as a penalty exacted upon a sinner by God; the patient has been visited by an avoidable misfortune, and his first response should be self-examination and moral atonement. A central dilemma in a religion is whether such divine action can or should be counteracted by independent human therapy. Some religions, particularly in their popularized versions, have answered negatively in some form, thus obstructing medical care. Some deviant Jewish sects have answered similarly, but the main doctrinal tradition is that although the ultimate cause of illness may be divine, the physical symptoms can be removed by human medical action. Some of the Talmudic rabbis deduced the legitimacy of medical work from the presence of physicians in the Old Testament; other rabbis derived an obligation to cure from the Biblical injunctions to save life. Over the centuries, considerable rabbinical lore accumulated to justify medical work and prescribe the moral conditions for its use.[9]

A theocentric explanation of the cause of illness can provide a powerful competitor to human medical care in the person of God's representatives. If God or other divine spirits caused illness, the most efficacious and prompt cure is direct communication through prayer or exorcising ritual. In many societies in the past and present, hospitals are ignored by the public or are sought out desperately only during advanced stages of illness, after the priest or prayer leader has been consulted first. But Judaism never has created this kind of competition. The prophet is the man of God in Jewish tradition, but the priest is simply a local functionary who performs rituals and has limited power to perform purifications.[10] A prophet can heal through prayer,[11] but of course prophets are few and direct intervention with God is unusual. The widespread folk religious belief that diseases can be cured by magic and exorcisms confers therapeutic power upon priests and prayer leaders, but Jewish theologians have long condemned such ideas.[12] So, according to Judaism, the afflicted must rely on doctors and not on priests.

Besides the aforementioned leprosaria, which were custodial institutions set apart from the community, the Hebrews had a few buildings to care for healthy and ill wayfarers. The simple huts for the ill (called *Beth Holim*) may have been the kernels of the modern Western hospital, but they lacked the extensive resources and specialized employees that have since become the hospital's distinctive characteristics. Hospitals did not develop on a large scale among the Jews for some centuries. They might have arisen in Palestine but for the Diaspora; the scattering of the Hebrews among small communities, the frequent migrations, and economic insecurity meant that enough resources, patients, and specialized hospital employees could not be combined at one site. Another reason for not developing hospitals in the Diaspora was the well-organized program of home care, which combined the efforts of doctor, rabbi, and neighbors. Many Jewish communities then and now have busy sick-visitation (*Bikkur Holim*) societies that provide therapy, prayer, and companionship.[13] A few small hospitals were created in ghettos and in Jewish villages for the needy and for persons without families,[14] but because of the strong preference for home care, large Jewish hospitals did not arise in the Diaspora until the eighteenth century.[15] But once the Jewish population returned to Israel, hospitals grew very rapidly, since resources and large patient clienteles were available, and nothing in the religion was unfavorable. The congeniality between the Jewish religion and most hospital functions can be seen today in establishments like Shaare Zedek in Jerusalem, where Orthodox routine and modern medical technique coexist within the same organization.

Western Christianity. As an heir of ancient Judaism, Western

Christianity has continued to emphasize the duty to provide charity and care to the needy. But since Christianity's psychology is different, it roots this duty in the voluntary act of brotherly love rather than in the commands of a sovereign God who promptly rewards and punishes.

As a prophet of the God of the Hebrews, Jesus performed many miraculous cures through direct prayer or a laying on of hands,[16] but this was simply a proof of his prophetic mission. His principal message was that loving and serving even the lowest man and tending the sick and needy are ways to share in the divine spirit and to earn God's favor.[17] Thus satisfaction in this world and salvation in the next could be earned through humane practical action. Emulating Jesus' word and deed, many followers performed home care of the sick or ran small hospitals, much like a combined ministry and bedside nursing.[18] Since Christianity has always been a religion of radical salvation, universal brotherly love, and missionary activity, its doctrine emphasizes charity and medical care to non-Christians as well as to Christians. After some initial hesitation, Jesus performed miraculous cures on Gentiles as well as on his fellow Jews, thus going beyond the exclusiveness of the ancient Hebrews.[19] At various times medical services run by the Church have given preferential treatment to Christians, but in the long run the policy has been less discriminatory than in the medical services affected by other religions, because of Christianity's doctrine and its atypical missionary aims.

Christianity has been the religion of extensive hospital construction, particularly during the Middle Ages. The initial conjunction of priestly and medical activity came from early Christianity's temporary assumption—shared with ancient Judaism and other contemporary religions—that sickness was at least partly due to sin,[20] and therefore that recovery depended at least partly on prayer and the patient's moral rehabilitation. So the patient was expected to call for the "elders of the church" to visit, pray, and anoint him.[21] Since Christianity developed as the religion of city-dwellers and itinerants, the Church soon needed to organize substitutes for the home care appropriate for rural communities organized around stable families. Thus priests, monks, nuns, and other Church functionaries began to set aside rooms for custodial care of patients, either in their own homes or in separate buildings; the religious or volunteers from the sect regularly cared for these patients.[22]

Christianity created for Europe and the Middle East a demand for hospitals. Monastic orders needed some means for care of their members that would replace the family. Frequent ceremonies in cathedrals and shrines intensified the urban concentration of the sect. Publicity given to shrines and other holy places stimulated long pilgrimages by people who needed housing and care *en route*. Holy wars against Islam led to a series of hospitals for soldiers throughout the Mediterranean.

Since Christianity combined humanitarian doctrine with Roman bureaucratic organization, it could develop a continent-wide program of fund-raising, hospital construction, and hospital routine along certain common patterns.[23] Hospital staffs were provided by a Christian innovation, monastic orders of men and women who would partake of the divine spirit and possibly earn personal salvation by unselfish humane service to the needy. The monastic orders became the specialists in the management and multiplication of formal organizations.[24] Like Jewish doctrine, Christian teachings never have conferred upon the priest or prayer leader the power to exorcise evil spirits or to secure divine assistance, and therefore the minister by himself has never been as powerful a competitor of the hospital in Christianity as in some other religions.

The Christian sects have had diverse effects on hospitals because of differing doctrines and ecclesiastic organizations. For example, the immediate effect of the Reformation was reduced investment of work and resources in hospitals. Catholicism had preached that sins could be expiated and souls saved through almsgiving, but Protestantism argued that salvation depended on faith and not works. Charitable donations by laymen for social services greatly diminished. Some Protestant denominations preached that almsgiving or donation to churches were good acts in themselves and were visible evidence of a donor's Christian soul. This viewpoint stimulated some charitable hospital development in a few Protestant countries, notably in England, but it lacked the pressure for large donations and extensive social services. Much of the available money went into nonmedical church work, such as missionary activity, buildings, and the salaries of staff. Protestantism lacked the large ecclesiastic structure to organize and man extensive medical programs in one's own country and in non-Christian countries;

it lacked a large specialized ministry for charitable work, since the Protestant Churches specialized in propagating the faith. This too caused a reduction in the scale of church-connected medical services.[25]

Eastern Christianity. All the foregoing refers to Catholicism and Protestantism. Byzantine Christianity developed very differently, and Orthodoxy today is a religion of liturgical observance. Imperatives governing action result from the doctrinal elaboration and legalistic thinking typical of the Western Church; the Orthodox are expected only to worship God and to love mankind. Rewards for good works and punishment for evil also are ideas peculiar to the legalistic West; universal salvation is implied by much of Orthodoxy. Eastern monks are contemplative rather than active, and the various Orthodox Churches usually have not organized welfare programs. The only exception has been the Greek Church, which occasionally has raised funds and participated in programs to house and feed refugees, a recurrent problem due to the country's wars and floods. Belief in brotherly love implies approval of medicine, but nothing in Orthodox doctrine or organization more specifically helps or hinders hospital affairs.[26] Because of the absence of indigenous incentives, certain of the elements necessary for Western styles of hospital organizations had to be imported.[27]

Islam. Like its Judaic ancestor, the Islamic faith contends that God has commanded men to perform certain duties, and He levies penalties or rewards upon the individual according to the latter's performance. Almsgiving to help the poor and needy is one of the five compulsory practices or "pillars" of Islam, and it is ordered by Allah. The individual is obligated to pay the legal and determined tax for the poor (called *zakat*), and he is also expected to give voluntary alms (called *sadaquat*). The alms-giver will thereby atone for his sins and be rewarded. Those who refuse to give alms or who ridicule alms-givers will be punished by Allah. The Koran does not contain as many references to illness as the Old and New Testaments, but it repeatedly commends purity of soul and body. Even though the Koran does not positively authorize the work of doctors, it can be interpreted as allowing it.[28]

Under Mohammed and the succeeding caliphs, *zakat* was institutionalized in very specific tax legislation to support assistance for the needy and other public charities. Meanwhile, as a form of *sadaquat*, wealthy Muslims began a still surviving tradition of willing parts of their estates to charitable funds (called *waqf*) to construct and maintain religious buildings. Because of the numerous large cities and population movements in the Arab empire, hospitals were needed. As part of their civic improvement program, the Abbasid caliphs enacted public health laws and used *zakat* tax money to build public hospitals. Some of the wealthy individuals donated *waqf* money to build hospitals, often adjacent to mosques. Meanwhile scientific knowledge was flowering throughout the Arab empire, Greek medicine was absorbed from the Mediterranean cities the Arab armies had conquered, and physicians welcomed the opportunity to study and work in the hospitals. The growth of medical education reinforced the need for hospitals. Since Islam did not develop a class of religious dedicated to humane service, its hospitals were run by laymen whose tasks and aims were influenced by religion; much earlier than in the West, where Christian hospital managements delayed entry by the lay physicians, the Islamic hospitals were the doctors' workshops.[29]

When the caliphate and Arab medicine declined, the hospital-building boom ended. In most Arab countries the compulsory poor tax was gradually abandoned. Islamic social welfare had depended on a united structure of State and Church; it could not survive a decline in the energy of the State functionaries in the partnership, and it could not survive the replacement of Arab officials by Turks with different goals. Unlike Christianity, Islam lacked an autonomous ecclesiastical structure that could preserve a welfare program in the face of a change in State policy. Some old hospitals continued in use for many centuries—the Maristan Kalaoun still functions in the bazaar district of Eastern Cairo[30]—and *waqf* money continued to maintain hospitals, but the previous impetus was gone and funds were insufficient for repair and improvement. While Christian hospitals for centuries could be run by monastic orders specializing in this work, the absence of monasticism or a comparable tradition of spiritually inspired personal service produced chronic problems of staffing and organizational survival. Almsgiving had always been defined primarily as charity to the poor, and the Koranic obligation could still be met by giving *baksheesh* to individual beggars and by endowing mosques; thus firm doctrinal support for hospital philanthropy was absent.

Meanwhile, the attenuation of official Muslim doctrine permitted the increasing influence of popularized doctrines that inhibited public use of hospitals and undermined their legitimacy. Islam had spread among Arab, African, and Asian populations with numerous folk beliefs; some of these beliefs were officially incorporated into Muslim thought and ritual, others were retained side by side for a time and then became part of a grass-roots Islam. One of these assumptions is that the world is full of supernatural spirits, some of which act against individuals either on their own initiative or at the bidding of other humans possessing magical power. This assumption is united with the official Judaic-Christian-Muslim doctrine that illness is at least partly a supernatural penalty for sin. As a result, for centuries many Muslim peasants and proletarians have believed that illnesses are due to the *jinn*, somebody's Evil Eye, or some other deviltry. But, according to popular Islam, such curses may be prevented or combatted by religious amulets or by rituals conducted by prayer leaders (called such names as *peers, maulvis, fuquara*). These clergymen perform rituals or prayers that are supposed to attract divine favor and result in cures, such as reading the Koran and allowing the breath "containing" the holy words to fall on the patient, applying to the patient spittle of persons who have just said their prayers, or giving "medicine" that consists of water containing ink dissolved from written Koranic words.[31] Folk medicine is not an official policy of Islam, but the absence of an ecclesiastic structure removes the possibility of enunciating policy or controlling the local prayer leaders. In contrast, the Catholic Church was able to control folk medical utilization of saints' shrines; the Church also stamped out folk beliefs in spirits and the Evil Eye, thus making Christianity almost unique among the world religions and eliminating from the West an important ideological basis of folk medicine.[32] Since the Muslim prayer leaders earn much of their income on a fee-for-service basis from these ceremonies, for centuries they have been competitors of the hospital and have discouraged their followers from seeking medical aid, particularly in rural areas.

Another popular deviation from original Muslim doctrine that is inimical to the existence of hospitals is fatalism. Like Judaism and early Christianity, Islam attributes misfortune to God's wrath, but its official doctrine is far more ambiguous whether misfortunes can be undone by any means other than petitioning God. Obviously the leaders of Arab medicine and of the early hospital program thought that human action was possible and proper, that physical illnesses are explicable and curable. But the Koran contained strongly predestinarian as well as free-will passages, some of the later denominations emphasized predestinarianism,[33] and this tendency has been propagated by popular Islam. The idea of submission to an omnipotent divine will that alone regulates and understands misfortunes is often presented by prayer leaders and seems meaningful when compared with the pessimistic life chances of the uncomprehending villager. If carried to their extreme, these ideas would deprive hospitals of their patients and existence; they are a principal reason for the empty beds in the rural areas of several Muslim countries. These ideas often lead to definitions of medical problems different from those of modern medicine; many Muslim villagers will not bring sick children or cases of trachoma to hospitals because it is assumed these are manifestations of the will of Allah rather than curable medical problems.[34]

Religions with mixed implications for the existence of hospitals—the cases of Buddhism and Hinduism. Christianity is unusual because it combines doctrine, ecclesiastic and monastic organization, the motivation of laymen, and historical opportunity—all in the necessary combination and intensity to produce an interest in and capacity for hospital creation and management that persist today. Some religions provide some supportive doctrines but lack other attributes with which the sect and its Church organization could be said to have produced a hospital system by themselves. Several religions have doctrines that are partial supports for the creation and utilization of hospitals, but other tendencies are contradictory. For example, certain Buddhist denominations preach doctrines that have provided part of the impetus for the hospital-building booms in Christianity and Islam, such as protection of life, the giving of alms, love for all beings, and self-sacrifice.[35] Some monks in Tibet and Ceylon work among the public as practitioners of ayurvedic medicine.

Although some Buddhist medical facilities have been created—

often in collaboration with modern *lay* governments for the needs of the monasteries themselves[36]—Buddhism has not translated its humanitarian premises into an active hospital program. Some of the reasons are doctrinal. Buddhism is the most voluntaristic of religions; it describes the Path to Nirvana, but everyone is left completely free and unscrutinized. In contrast, the aforementioned Western religions that have produced hospital programs command or (in Christianity) exhort men to be charitable, threaten penalties for selfishness and for apathy, require personal service for the sick (in Judaism and Christianity) and prescribe a continuous divine and social examination of each individual's performance. Buddhism urges relief from illness—indeed the avoidance of suffering is its central problem—but illness is not considered an independent and modifiable deviation in an otherwise satisfactory social existence. Rather, all experiences are part of an undifferentiated state of suffering, one cannot make rapid and enduring cures of disease alone, and the real solution is to embark on the Path of meditation and self-improvement that will overcome all forms of suffering together. Buddhists may be more apathetic about seeking medical care than are members of Western religions, even Islam.[37] In the Hebrew and Christian religions, the hospital staffing problem was solved by the doctrine promising salvation through humanitarian service, but while Buddhism commends such service, the Path to Nirvana can be secured only through self-management.

Buddhism has not translated its humanitarian premises into a hospital program for reasons of Church organization as well as doctrine. Many of the Christian monastic orders have specialized in medical and nursing care, since the Church is organized for public service as well as for missionary work and for the self-improvement of its members. But since Buddhism is so concerned with teaching the Path, most of its numerous monks and lay female disciples are occupied in public and monastic education, fundraising, and self-improvement. One reason for the hospital boom in Christendom and Islam was the organizational skill of the Church and of lay religious associations in seeking large donors and in saving and managing large amounts of money and real property. But Buddhist doctrine condemns worldly ostentation in favor of poverty and the spiritual life, and this may inhibit its leaders from developing the kind of organizational acquisitiveness and fiscal management necessary for an expanding hospital program.

Finally, unlike the aforementioned Western religions, Buddhism has not had to solve great problems of mass care. Unlike Christianity and (to a lesser degree) Islam, it has been a religion of peaceful rural areas rather than a religion of crowded cities. It spread in highly familistic societies, where home care of the sick is taken for granted. Unlike Christianity and Islam it did not stimulate incessant movement by the public.

Another religion that produced contradictory tendencies was Hinduism. The ancient Vedic and Brahmanical sects of India developed a theory about the nature and regulation of both the total universe and the life of the individual. Included in the sacred Sanskrit literature were the books of the Ayur-Veda, which described the causes and cures of various diseases. Since life, health, and good will were encouraged by some doctrines, medicine could be applied to effectuate cures. Some Brahmans, members of the caste entrusted with sacred knowledge, became ayurvedic physicians.

Thus the ancient faith simply provided medical knowledge and legitimized therapy. It did not preach duties of social service or charity,[38] nor did it have ecclesiastic functionaries or monks eager or able to develop some doctrinally worthy or publicly visible program of good works. Some ancient Hindu ideas were barriers to the development of hospitals for the public. Doctrines about caste made it difficult for large numbers of employees of different ranks to collect together and collaborate; these doctrines prevented the predominantly Brahman doctors from treating the public. (Caste taboos continue to complicate Indian hospital administration today.) The medical facility described in the *Charaka-Samhita* of the first century A.D. sounds not like a hospital but like an annex to a doctor's office, where he could give intensive care to a single Brahman patient.[39] Besides its particularistic implications barring mass therapy to the public, Hinduism's doctrine of *Karma* could be interpreted as discouraging public use of medical services. This image of an uncontrollable and endless cycle of life is used by the Indian lower classes today as a rationalization for apathy toward medical care.[40]

By themselves, neither Buddhism nor Hinduism could have produced hospitals, but by a historical coincidence, the two were combined and joined to a secular program when King Asoka of India (274–236 B.C.) became converted to Buddhism. As the head of a government, Asoka had to cope with practical health problems, such as the care of wayfarers. As a Buddhist, he was determined to translate principles of charity and the preservation of life into government action; as a convert to a nonviolent religion and impelled to atone for his previous military destructiveness, he was motivated to create a far more active public welfare program than would any ordinary Buddhist leader.[41] As king of India, he was heir to ayurvedic medicine and the prior experience in small-scale medical organization. So, much like the later Islamic caliphs (who, unlike him, were religious as well as political functionaries), Asoka used state resources to develop a series of hospitals designed to solve human problems for religious ends. Some of these hospitals for the public were run by the central government, some by towns, and some by monasteries.[42]

Indian hospitals eventually lapsed. They had required a combination of Buddhist ethics, Hindu medical technique, and decisive State leadership. But after Asoka, traditional Brahmanical Hinduism gradually revived in India and Buddhism disappeared. Meanwhile, the government weakened, and no ecclesiastical structure existed to continue the welfare policy. Some of Asoka's hospitals survived for a few more centuries (the last in, significantly, Buddhist Ceylon) and some successor hospitals lasted until the Middle Ages, but the impetus was gone. Meanwhile, both the ontological and medical doctrines of Hinduism were transformed by popular animistic ideas.

Religions of taboo and their obstruction of hospitals. Most societies in the world have had religions inimical to the creation and utilization of any type of hospital. Since illness and concern with possible death are central sources of suffering in every society, every religion has some prominent doctrines about the possible causes of illness, and from these most religions derive implications about appropriate responses.[43] Some religions and their social orders emphasize ethics; others are premised on taboo. Ethical religions define suffering as a diffuse condition involving many problems; they do not promise simple solutions; and they prescribe complex ceremonials and devotions under priestly guidance. In many such schemes, Western medicine has a place. But religions of taboo picture a world following simple and magical procedures: they specify the acts that must be avoided and the enemies that must be mollified; violation of any taboo arouses simple punishment by the enemy or censor, and this punishment can be exorcised easily. The priest identifies the cause of the suffering and employs the appropriate magic of exorcism.[44]

Religions of taboo are inimical to modern Western medicine. Illness is thought to be a principal punishment for violation of a taboo: many sects attribute the majority of diseases to gods, spirits, and magical acts by malevolent humans with special powers. As in the case of popular Islam and popular Hinduism, the right kind of exorcism or magic can cure that disease by combatting its ultimate cause, and therefore priests, prayer leaders, and folk doctors using magic (alone or with other remedies) are fully qualified to do everything necessary. Since most of these religions believe that diseases occur suddenly, such societies look for simple and sudden cures that can be dispensed during ambulatory or home visits.[45]

Since the patient wishes total relief from both physical and psychological suffering, the Western-style doctor cannot be accepted as a substitute for the folk practitioner who deals with all sorts of suffering at once. The Western patient has become accustomed to transactions with a series of functionally specific institutions; most realize that the doctor can deal with only some areas of suffering, and that the priest must be consulted for others. But such functional specificity between medicine and religion is only beginning to be learned in underdeveloped countries today, and many patients still seek a practitioner who can relieve their total undifferentiated state of suffering. The doctor and the hospital are at a competitive disadvantage vis à vis the omniscient folk practitioner who can supposedly locate and manipulate the ultimate causes. The doctor can only tell the patient that a physical event occurred in his body; but the patient's suffering may persist, since he may still worry about why the event beset him and whether it will recur, two problems of suffering that are religious. Unable to answer the apparently basic question and sometimes making the admissions of uncertainty required by the ethics of his profession, the Western-style doctor may appear very dissatisfying.[46]

Selective use of the hospital, particularly the outpatient clinic, may be possible. Most primitive medico-religious theories exempt certain health problems, particularly injuries, from the magical category. For these, purely physical causes and cures are accepted, and the medicine man is not consulted. The family may employ certain well-known methods of first aid, surgery, or herbal medicine, or it may employ a tribal specialist.[47] Inhabitants of underdeveloped countries sometimes bring these nonmagical conditions to the Western-style hospital or health center while relying upon the folk doctor for the illnesses defined as magical by folk belief. The patient will not tell the Western-style doctor about the magical illnesses that are deemed beyond his competence.[48]

Before Western-style hospital services can expand in such societies the folk beliefs from the start must define only a few diseases as magical; or, on the other hand, public opinion must transfer most illnesses out of the magical category, as a result of theological redefinition and critical comparisons of the performance of the scientific and folk doctors. Above all, the society must develop functional specificity among the social institutions for the alleviation of suffering; the patient must learn how to use both doctors and clergymen. As societies with religions of taboo modernize, selective use of the Western-type medical services grows. Enough patients profit from surgery and from antibiotics, and the news spreads that these techniques have their own "manna." Eventually supernatural manna is deemed irrelevant to the treatment of any disease. Structural differentiation and secularization thereby increase.

In systems of interdependent elements, one variable is affected in turn by those it has initially influenced. Religion not only affects medical care, but changes in medical institutions help bring about changes in religion. I have not investigated the effects of changing medical behavior upon religion, but the following seem plausible. As selective referral to the hospital grows, faith in exorcism may be replaced by belief in natural remedies of all sorts, and religions of taboo may evolve into faiths emphasizing personal ethics, worship, and ritual. As fewer members of religious orders work in hospitals and as the denomination's authority over medical services declines, then the influence of the denomination in the population may decline; the denomination's emphasis on works and worldly sacrifice may be replaced by stress on worship, ritual, and personal deportment; the laity may become more powerful and the clergy relatively less powerful; and the society may experience fewer disputes among denominations or between the Church and anticlericals.

Ownership and Direction

Societies with one principal religion. Once many European hospitals were owned by Churches or by monastic orders. Each was part of a complex of buildings including a large church and a cloister, and it had the same architectural appearance, with high ceilings, frescoes, altars, and carved wooden beds resembling Gothic pews. Somewhat modernized, such ancient wards can still be seen in Spain, Italy, Belgium, and France. Church ownership of a public general hospital is now very rare.

Between the Reformation and the twentieth century, many hospitals in Christian countries were owned by associations of laymen identified with the Catholic Church or with a Protestant denomination. Some of the previously Church-owned hospitals were taken over amicably and expanded by such associations. Participating in the management and financing of hospitals was a favorite charity of devout Catholic and Protestant laymen for several centuries, in accordance with the Christian doctrines mentioned earlier. Hospital ownership by private associations of devout laymen is still common in countries with several competing religions, but one can still find a few examples in the one-religion countries where the majority of hospitals has been nationalized.

In most countries today—and in all with one prevalent religion —general hospitals are owned by governments. In underdeveloped countries, the owner is usually the national Ministry of Health; in Europe, usually it is a municipality, province, or national health insurance fund. Many of these hospitals were created by governments, but some were acquired from religious owners. In some northern European countries hospitals were seized during the

Reformation along with other Church property. In a few such as France, the hospitals were transferred at a later date during anti-clerical revolutions. Even in countries that have been free of anti-clerical revolutions, such as Spain and Italy, Church-owned general hospitals have gradually been transferred into the hands of private associations or municipalities who can undertake the burdensome financing and management more easily than the Church or a religious order. Meanwhile, many private hospitals once owned and managed by associations of laymen have gradually been transferred voluntarily to the municipalities, which can finance and manage them better.

The Church does not always resist the government take-over of these hospitals, since the official establishment of the Church in one-religion countries means that any government social service in some respects remains tinged with a religious aura. If the Church or the affiliated lay associations tried to retain ownership, it would suffer from the brickbats that are usually directed by every society against the financing and staffing of its hospitals.[49] When the hospitals are in the hands of the State, the Church can concentrate its limited personnel and money on activities that will influence the population's religious devotion more directly, such as ceremonies and parochial education.

The continuing influence of the national religion on the everyday management of these government hospitals depends on certain conditions. First, there must be some kind of ecclesiastical structure that formulates ethical and social policy, produces an *esprit de corps* among the clergy, and induces unity and continuity of action. Clergymen in sects with only a rudimentary or no Church organization do not seem to be drawn into hospital affairs in any regular way. For example, in the Muslim countries I visited, hospital directors did not report any continuous contact with any Church functionaries; Islam's system is decentralized, in contrast to the hierarchies of Catholicism and Anglicanism, which seem to maintain a continuous nationwide interest in hospital questions. A second condition for Church involvement in hospital affairs is doctrinal inclusion of health and social welfare in the religious mission. In some countries with State religions, such as Greece, the Church's mission is conceived as liturgical observance and doctrinal instruction. Such Churches may maintain a regular contact with the Ministry of Education but not with the health services, so long as hospitals do not impinge on any rituals. A third condition for Church influence is that the ancient hospitals (if any) were transferred gradually and amicably, no radical secularizing revolution ever occurred, and hospital administrators, government officials and the public assume either voluntarily or fatalistically that the Church shall be consulted about many local affairs. Church influence is highest in Spain and Italy but considerably less in most of France because of this third condition.

Several channels of influence exist. For example, in Spain and Italy, each public hospital is governed by a board of local laymen. Rarely will a priest belong, but in all of Spain and most of Italy no board member, hospital administrator, or chief of a medical service will be appointed if he is unacceptable to the Archbishop. Often one or two board members will be active in Catholic lay associations and will be close to the hierarchy. Probably such members do not act as messengers or Church representatives, since apparently the hierarchy is not concerned with the details of daily hospital life. But these members' viewpoint will be conditioned by their religious affiliations, their influence within the Board is probably based on their good standing with the Established Church, they are alert to any hospital policies unacceptable to the Church, and they are often the board members whom the Church functionaries will contact in case of questions or complaints. The Church may also influence hospital management through the medical and nursing staffs. Some of the doctors may belong to religious associations as well as to the lay professional organ; in the meetings and business of the association, the leadership will be in touch with Church functionaries, and some policy decisions will take into consideration the Church's moral teachings and organizational aims. Since many of the head nurses on wards may be nuns, nursing service may be counted on to follow whatever Church policies are announced. In anticlerical countries, such as France, the nursing nun may be the only remaining channel of Church influence in the hospital.

Where Church influence is customary, usually it is exercised informally and sparingly. In Christian countries, the Church hierarchy is kept informed of the hospital management's plans for expansion and new construction. The Church may comment occasionally in its newspapers if it suspects declines in medical services or in Christian morals. But in the daily management of the hospital the Church defers to the doctors and administration: the increasing secularization and specialization of medical knowledge during the modernization of society deprives the Church of the requisite expert knowledge and creates a division between medical and religious work.

Societies with more than one principal religion. The Church can gain little by managing hospitals in a society where everyone is a nominal member. It can only lose, since complaints about services would contribute to anticlericalism. However, the pattern is different in those countries where religions are mixed and where Church functionaries are concerned with interdenominational competition, such as countries with large Protestant and Catholic groups and many countries with Christian minorities amidst Muslim, Buddhist, or primitive majorities. In such a competitive setting, transfer of hospitals to the government would not be a welcome liberation from a financial and administrative burden, but it would be a diminution of Church functions and a loss of a highly visible evidence of good works. At a time of personal crisis when they seek explanations and solace, patients might be exposed to secular or rival sectarian influences. Losing control over hospitals might reduce the denomination's power to secure and keep members. Consequently, in such countries many general hospitals remain in private and Church-dominated hands.[50]

Hospital decisions sometimes become involved in the evangelical strategies of Churches in such multireligion countries. Catholic and Protestant hospital associations sometimes compete to establish new hospitals in towns that previously have none or only public hospitals. As a result, in a few towns of Holland there are trios of small hospitals—public, Protestant, and Catholic—where a neutral national planner might have established only one large hospital. This is one of the reasons why over one-third of Holland's general hospital beds are in hospitals with less than 125 beds.[51] In most of these the burden of supporting a hospital requires the various Protestant denominations to join in supplying patients, staff, and money in the same hospitals. But a few countries—notably the United States—not only have created many Protestant denominations but have made them wealthy enough to establish their own private hospitals. Some underdeveloped countries have many different Protestant hospitals as well, because they are owned by missionary societies drawing money and staff from the numerous affluent denominations in America and Great Britain.

Does this religious competition in the creation and management of hospitals interfere with medical practice? In medical care in the more modernized and secularized countries, the common conditioning and goals of the medical profession are a powerful integrating force. Once erected by the Churches, hospitals are managed by lay administrators and by doctors who often cooperate in order to promote both their own organizations' efficiency and the public interest that they perceive as their overriding responsibility. For example, in Holland the nationwide Catholic and Protestant hospital associations cooperate (often by naming a common representative) when negotiating fees with the health insurance funds, when bargaining collectively with hospital employees, and when providing advice to the national Ministry of Health. For twenty years the Catholic, Protestant, and other private hospitals of Amsterdam have had standing committees (recently expanded into an organized foundation) to discuss issues, promote cooperation in personnel matters and avoid raiding, negotiate with sick funds, conduct public relations and health education of the public, conduct research, and (possibly during future years) develop central purchasing. Referral of difficult patients from one hospital to another is common; in one of the large cities, at the time of writing, the Catholic, Protestant, and public hospitals are conferring about proposals to develop a regional hospital system in which individual hospitals would specialize in different tasks and would be integrated into one system of referral and consultation, instead of each covering all services. In some of the Dutch towns with both Protestant and Catholic hospitals, important specialists who could not be fully employed in one alone, such as cardiologists, are hired by both and follow a work schedule agreed upon by the two directors.

Sectarian ownership is dysfunctional for hospitals and medical service if sectarian conflict is severe and integrating mechanisms are weak. For example, many Middle Eastern cities under the Ottoman Empire were organized according to extreme communalism. Each sect had its own churches, schools, medical services,

clubs, economic and political institutions, and residential neighbor-
hoods. The visitor to any Middle Eastern city today sees hospitals
that now or formerly served each sect, with staff, patients, and
financial support drawn from that sect. But collaboration among
sectarian hospitals was minimal. A doctor might have staff appointments with both a sectarian hospital and one where neutral
professional values predominated (such as the university teaching
hospital), but an appointment at another sectarian hospital was
unusual.

The conditions minimizing the medical diseconomies of communalism in Holland have been absent in the Middle East. First, the
Churches and sect members have often been very hostile to each
other, particularly since the rise of anti-European Muslim national-
ism since World War II, and this spirit affected doctors and hospitals. Second, while Holland is a homogeneous country that unites
in crises, such underlying social integration has been absent in the
Middle East. The different sects have had little personal contact,
few common activities, incompatible economic interests, different
languages and modes of life, opposing foreign reference groups
during international crises, and demagogic leaders who intensified
controversies. If protests come from other sects, such as complaints
that the hospital was not available to them, the leadership of the
sect owning the hospital would ignore them. Instead, the leadership would heed only reports from its own brethren about whether
the hospital was satisfactorily serving the interests of that sect. A
third reason for the separation of sectarian hospitals in the Middle
East has been absence of the professional organization and *esprit
de corps* that are so striking in the Dutch medical profession.
Instead, doctors in many Middle Eastern cities have been divided
in struggles to earn livelihoods.[52]

The national State can be a mechanism for modernizing sectarian medical services, as well as professional associations. Some
Middle Eastern governments have intervened in hospital management in order to compel cooperation and efficiency. For example,
the Egyptian government has been moving toward nationalization
and coordination of all large general hospitals. Among the decrees
adopted in the early 1960s was a requirement that the Christian
and Jewish hospitals in Cairo and Alexandria provide educational
and staff opportunities for young Muslim doctors who outnumber

the openings available in the public hospitals.

Sectarian hospitals can be coordinated when the denominations themselves decide to collaborate instead of using the hospitals as instruments of competitive proselytizing. For example, after Ecumenical Council Vatican II, officials of the Vatican and of the World Council of Churches (representing numerous Protestant and Eastern Orthodox denominations) began to plan better coordination of the numerous hospitals operated throughout the world by their missionary societies. When several sectarian hospitals are located nearby, techniques and research facilities may be shared, some staff appointments might be joint, and a division of labor may be created in services.

Recruitment of Hospital Employees

Religious. Christianity is the only religion with a large number of Church functionaries specializing in hospital care. For centuries, many of the world's nurses and hospital administrators were Catholic monks or nuns,[53] and nuns still do much nursing throughout the world. In a few countries the Catholic Church sponsors nursing Brotherhoods, but they are small and declining.[54] Communities of Protestant Deaconesses were founded during the nineteenth century and still work in some hospitals, primarily in Switzerland, Germany, and Holland.

There is little sociological evidence about recruitment into orders. The consensus of impressions among my clerical and lay informants was that novices tend to come from large, closely-knit and religious families from the lower middle and lower classes in towns and rural areas, and that novices have depended heavily upon their parish priests for advice.

The provision of religious nurses for hospitals is a simple administrative procedure and is nearly the same in all countries that use them. The nuns or Deaconesses are trained and supported by the central administration of the order.[55] In supplying nurses, the executives of the order give priority to hospitals owned by the

Church, by a religious association, or by the order itself. In some Catholic countries, tradition and budgetary inability to pay a full staff of lay nurses lead the public hospitals to ask for a certain number of nuns from any orders that they prefer. The executives of the order then negotiate a contract with the hospital. The order agrees to supply a certain number of religious for a monthly fee per individual. The hospital agrees to provide food, housing, a chapel, money and materials for clothing, and free time. Contracts last for a few years, such as three or five; they are usually, but not always, renewed. The principal difference among countries and among orders and hospitals in the same country is the size of the hospitals' payments. Poorer countries and poorer hospitals pay lower fees. All nuns and most Deaconesses are sent to hospitals in groups, but sometimes one or two Deaconesses secure jobs at a hospital with the approval of their superiors.

Officials of nursing orders in several countries told me that they like to assign nuns and Deaconesses to the public hospitals, since there the religious have much direct contact with the working class and elderly and can create for them a beneficial spiritual atmosphere.[56] Although nuns rarely do explicit proselytizing in public hospitals nowadays, it is believed that their presence will create a beneficial Christian milieu for people experiencing emotional stress, and that they can provide instant religious help for any Catholic in need. In the Catholic countries of Latin Europe, the Church is ever concerned that materialistic living conditions and left-wing ideologies threaten the morality and salvation of the average citizen, and therefore the presence of nuns in the public hospitals is an important Church mission. Occasionally in Spain and Italy orders agree to send nuns to the private profit-earning hospitals owned and managed by doctors; partly they wish to provide a religious atmosphere for upper class people whom they believe otherwise lead excessively secular and materialistic lives, partly they wish to reward Catholic doctors who have been friendly to the nuns in their public hospital duties. Some nuns in Spain and Italy work in private profit-earning clinics owned by the order itself as a way of earning money for the order's charitable activities.

The presence of religious in public hospitals depends on the ratio between supply and demand. While hospital jobs have been increasing steadily, the rate of recruitment into religious vocations has been declining in most countries.[57] The reasons have been a mixture of the changing opportunities for women and the changing function of religion in actual daily life. Freer marital and occupational opportunities for women have enabled more to adjust satisfactorily in the world. Meanwhile throughout Europe increasing urbanization, education, and worldly interests have curtailed the extent and intensity of ecclesiastic influence over women. Piety may have changed by becoming less devotional and a matter predominantly of ideology and ritual; thus a woman may remain pious without feeling that Christianity calls her to a religious vocation of self-sacrifice and total service. The Protestant Deaconesses have had more serious recruitment problems than the Catholic nuns.

To economize, the administrators in multireligion countries have been withdrawing nuns and Deaconesses from public hospitals in order to concentrate them in the understaffed religious hospitals, in old age hospices, and in home care.[58] The visitor to Germany and Switzerland once saw many Deaconesses and nuns in the public hospitals, but today he sees no nuns there and only an occasional Deaconess. If nearly all the country's general hospitals are public, as in Latin Europe, the administrators of the order attempt to concentrate the nuns in those parts of the public hospital where their presence is deemed most important from a missionary viewpoint, such as obstetrics, geriatrics, and internal medicine.

Nurses. Modern professional nursing began during the nineteenth century partly as a result of the challenges to religious nursing by the increased secularization of society and the burgeoning of medical science. In no country could the religious nursing orders recruit fast enough to keep pace with the increased number of jobs; in the Protestant countries, the recruitment ceiling was low and therefore nearly all the hospital nurses were unskilled and undisciplined laywomen. Medical progress and hospital reorganization created demands for technical skill and commitment to secular work that nuns and Deaconesses were believed to possess insufficiently. The founders of modern professional nursing, such as Florence Nightingale, wished to create a lay occupation that could recruit more members than the orders, that would develop maximum technical skill and work discipline, but that would preserve the humane dedication and moral standards of the religious. Since many of these founders were devout Christians—often Protestants—they conceived nursing as a lay career serving both social and Christian ends.[59]

Among the categories of lay hospital employee, it is the nurse whose job seems to possess most strongly the aura of humane personal service and therefore whose numbers today are still most affected by the religious milieu of the society. The Christian legitimation of personal service to sick strangers probably results in a higher rate of recruitment into lay professional and practical nursing in Christian than in non-Christian countries at the same level of economic development. In some of the countries where Church teachings are influential and where other facilitating conditions are present, such as Eire and the Philippine Islands, enough nurses are recruited for hospitals' needs, in contrast to the unfilled jobs nearly everywhere else. In the developed countries, devout persons may be overrepresented in nursing compared to the rest of the population; for example, church-going Protestants and devout Roman Catholic girls may be proportionately overrepresented in American and French nursing.[60] In a large sample of American nursing students, the weaker the belief and practice of religion, the weaker the commitment to a nursing career and the greater the wastage from nursing school.[61] In Puerto Rico, as in the aforementioned American and French surveys, lay nurses rated service to God among the principal reasons for entering nursing.[62]

In the non-Christian countries, the Christian minority often is overrepresented in graduate and practical nursing, although possibly not among the auxiliaries. For example, in a recent class at the Nursing College of Baragwanath Hospital in Johannesburg twenty-six of the twenty-seven African girls were Christians. Of the 977 graduate nurses trained in Lebanon between 1905 and 1955, all but 4 percent were Christian. At the time of my visit to the French Faculty of Medicine in Beirut in 1961, thirty-one of the thirty-four students in graduate nursing were Christians, and only one was Muslim. Of the 583 graduate nurses in Muslim Iraq in 1955, only one-third were Muslim, and most of the rest were Christians. For many years the only nurses in Muslim Indonesia were Christians, and the Christians are still statistically overrepresented. In 1952 in Muslim East Pakistan, only about 30 percent of the students were Muslim, and most of the others were Christian. Until recently, a large majority of the nurses in Hindu India were Christian, and the Christians are still overrepresented.[63]

Part of the explanation for differential recruitment is directly religious: Christian young girls and their families may be less repelled by a job requiring personal and physical service for sick strangers than are Muslims, Hindus, Jews, and others. Other reasons for such an imbalance are indirectly religious: for many years the mission hospitals and Red Cross ran all the nursing schools in underdeveloped countries, and the Western-oriented, better-educated and more urban Christians had higher representations in those student bodies than in the total population. For example, for many years, the Lebanese Christians got better education and more professional jobs than the Muslims, since most of the schools, including the aforementioned French Faculty, were run by churches.[64] However, in those countries where nursing traditionally has been perceived as a servile lower class job, Christians will not be overrepresented in it; for example, the Coptic Christians have been a better-educated upper class minority in Egypt, and although they have been overrepresented in medicine, they are probably underrepresented in nursing. In those underdeveloped countries with recruitment differentials between the Christian minority and the non-Christian majority, doubtless the differences will diminish as the latter acquires more education and as nursing increasingly becomes—regardless of denomination—a professional career with an administrative and scientific image.

Recruitment differences exist among the non-Christian religions, because of ethical beliefs and different definitions of the status of women. For example, as I shall say in greater detail in the next chapter, popular Islam has restricted the educational and occupational opportunities of women. Therefore the Indian subcontinent before partition depended primarily on Christian and Hindu nurses, with few Muslims in this work. After partition and population shifts, Muslim Pakistan was left with only four hundred graduate nurses for a population of 76,000,000.[65] In present-day India, very few Indian nurses are Muslim, despite the presence of a large Muslim minority. Far more Indian nurses are Hindu.[66]

Until recently, many countries depended heavily upon devotional motives for recruitment into lay professional nursing. For example, an English nurse told me of the importance of religion for herself and her peers before World War II:

> Nurses then were devoted to a vocation. The majority of nurses were devoted Anglicans, and we went to church in the morning. Nurses would willingly work very long hours, since this was our lives. Many nurses would use their days off making clothing for poor children and similar charities. For student nurses, religion was an important part of our lives. As students, we regularly went to chapel services in the morning and again in the evening at 9 P.M. The nursing schools were attached to voluntary hospitals, and all these teaching voluntary hospitals were attached to the Anglican Church.

But in England and some other countries, church attendance and ecclesiastic influence over the population have been declining for some decades,[67] and fewer people make vocational decisions primarily according to religious reasons. Many recruits still come from the more devout groups in the society, but this minority is becoming smaller; the average recruit may remain more devout than the average citizen, but certain nonreligious motivations will play a larger role than earlier in her career decisions. All this simply continues the secularization of the West and the laicization of graduate nursing, two trends that are many decades old. Centuries ago, the rise of secular medicine injected lay doctors into the Church-owned hospitals; now the increasing secular character of recruitment and training in nursing is injecting more secular-minded personnel into nursing service. This creates problems in nursing services of many public hospitals in Latin Europe, where nuns continue to be matrons and ward sisters. (See pp. 58–60 for a more detailed discussion.)

Physicians. The effects of religion upon the recruitment of doctors into hospitals have varied historically according to the relationship between Church and hospital and the relationship between religious ideology and medical practice. In the primitive and underdeveloped countries that were long without hospitals, it was taken for granted that scientific doctors should work in private office visits and in home visits. In ancient Islam and ancient India, the hospitals from their start were the workshops of lay doctors. But centuries of Church ownership and management complicated the entry of doctors into European hospitals.

Until the Middle Ages, most European doctors worked in their offices or in patients' homes. The monastic orders provided spiritual guidance and custodial care in the hospitals, but therapy was meager. While clinical therapy was progressing among the Arabic and Byzantine heirs of Greek medicine, it lagged in Catholic Europe. The first hospital doctors were monks who decided to add some scientific knowledge to their spiritual and nursing techniques; from various parts of Europe, they attended courses based on Arabic and Greek medicine at new schools in Salerno and elsewhere in Italy. Whether the monks should practice medicine instead of confining themselves to traditional hospital nursing was debated within the Church. Conservative theologians argued that, since Churchmen should specialize in the soul and not in the unworthy body, monks should not become doctors; thus, they said, medical practice should be excluded from Church organizations, such as hospitals. Eventually a compromise developed. Monks could help mankind by means of medical knowledge but could not draw blood; consequently, monks could become doctors specializing in internal medicine and chemotherapy, but surgery would be left to laymen. As a result, hospitals became places for diagnosing and treating the sick, and healthy persons were no longer allowed to lodge there. By the late Middle Ages, many laymen were graduating from the medical curricula of the new universities, and the Church and municipalities were happy to let them help cope with the heavy patient load in the hospitals; the laymen did all the surgery, much of the internal medicine, and occasional autopsies. Gradually hospital medicine became entirely a lay occupation, while nursing remained under the control of the nuns. Christianity's distinction between the immortal soul and the unworthy body thus permitted the entry into Church organizations of a lay occupation specializing in the body and possessing considerable freedom as long as its technical work raised no theological challenges. Many Italian Renaissance bishops were patrons of the new sciences, and lay hospital doctors and clinical scholars worked in a favorable atmosphere, disturbed by only occasional doctrinal or administrative controversies. The Reformation strengthened the lay hospital doctor in various ways: governments weakened the monastic orders and religious foundations and sometimes nationalized the hospitals; witch-hunts and the destruction of saints' shrines eliminated his principal competitors.[68]

By now the Western-style doctor throughout the world seems a highly secularized professional who is recruited into his career and into the public hospital by motivations other than religious devotion, but religion may have certain latent effects or may correlate with some determinants of recruitment. Doctors everywhere are recruited from those social groups that have the necessary education, ambitions, and personal *savoir-faire*. In many non-Christian countries, such as Egypt and Lebanon, the Christian minorities are heavily overrepresented in medicine. At the time I visited the French Faculty in Beirut in 1961, 249 out of the 296 medical students were Christian, and only forty-one were Muslim. Of the sixty-seven women graduated from the two Lebanese medical schools between 1931 and 1954, fifty-seven have been Christian and ten Muslim. Of the fifty-two women doctors practicing in Lebanon in 1955, forty were Christian and twelve Muslim.[69] Official Lebanese census figures have not been issued since 1944, when 53 percent were supposed to be Christian, but differential birth rates and emigration now have made the population over 50 percent Muslim.

Perhaps one reason for the medical recruitment patterns is the social psychology of religious affiliations, although research would be needed to establish this definitely. In underdeveloped countries at present, Christianity may be more compatible with worldly activity and scientific thought than some of the popular religions described at the beginning of this chapter. Another reason is non-doctrinal but is the social consequence of Christians' minority status. In most underdeveloped countries the Christians are usually better educated than the rest of the population and come from Western-oriented families whose style of life provides the personality and ambitions to enter Western-style careers.[70]

Auxiliaries and domestics. The relationship between religion and recruitment into auxiliary and domestic hospital work may be the reverse of the relationship for doctors. In all countries, this work seems a form of unskilled manual labor. Since they are better educated and of higher class status than their fellow citizens, Christians may be underrepresented among auxiliaries and domestics in underdeveloped countries. In the more developed countries, possibly regular churchgoers and members of evangelical sects are overrepresented among older auxiliaries.[71]

Recruitment into religious hospitals. In the countries of mixed religions, where competition induces the Churches or religious associations to create and maintain hospitals with a definite religious image, the lay personnel are recruited according to religious as well as professional considerations. Self-selection does most of the screening; usually only doctors, nurses, and others of that denomination apply for work in a hospital that is conspicuously connected with a particular Church in its public image and internal operations. Church functionaries sometimes help recruit employees, primarily by encouraging parishioners to enter the nursing schools or auxiliary staffs of a nearby religious hospital. Religious devotionalism may be particularly important in the self-selection of graduate nurses; in each European religious hospital that I visited, virtually all the lay graduate nurses were members of that denomination and had attended a Church-sponsored school of nursing, and my informants thought this was usual everywhere. In Germany, the lay graduate nurse who has attended a Church-sponsored school usually belongs to a Church-affiliated *Mutterhaus* or *Schwesternschaft* and tends to be assigned to one of the denominational hospitals.

Devotionalism may recruit some of the doctors. "I came because I believe deeply in religion, because I am a Protestant of the heart," a chief of service in a German religious hospital told me. Career opportunities are also a motive. Religious hospitals usually have small medical staffs, and many service chiefs tend to stay throughout their careers; religious hospitals develop a family-like intimacy by appointing service chiefs at a young age and hoping to keep them for decades. While a young doctor may spend many years slowly ascending the hierarchy of the public hospitals, he can become a service chief early by filling an opening left by a retirement in a religious hospital. "Julius Caesar said, 'Better to be first in the village than second in Rome,' " a young service chief in a Swiss religious hospital told me. He had transferred there from a large cantonal hospital, where his age peers were still *chefs de clinique*. Selection along religious lines is never dogmatic and complete, since hospitals must run according to professional medical standards and since there are never enough good applicants for religious hospital jobs. Therefore in America, Holland, Germany, and some other countries with mixed religions, denominational hospitals usually have some doctors and other employees of other faiths.

The hospital itself does some screening; during pre-employment interviews, some directors emphasize that the applicant must be aware of and never detract from the special moral atmosphere of the hospital. The screening involves some controls. A few directors of Western European religious hospitals said they would ask for the resignation of any doctor or nurse whose behavior in his personal life or private practice would damage the public reputation or internal harmony of the hospital—particularly publicized sexual scandals or the performance of abortions—but such cases rarely occur because of the prior self-selection and screening.

Performance of Lay Employees

The hospitals in Catholic, Protestant, Muslim, Jewish, and other countries have different medical policies in certain services. (See pp. 60–72.) Therefore, comparisons among these countries show that doctors and nurses perform different acts. Does the religious milieu of a country produce differences in the ways that doctors and lay nurses perform the *same* acts? It is difficult to isolate the effects of religious inputs, since in cross-national comparison they are confounded with other economic and organizational inputs that produce great differences in medical performance: the Protestant countries are the most developed economically and scientifically, while the Muslim, Buddhist, and Hindu countries are least developed.

Doctors. If all other variables of social structure are held constant, the effects of countries' religious milieux on doctors' performance of the *same* medical acts may be minimal. Modern medicine is a powerful international social system, and doctors increasingly learn the same values and techniques. Since most doctors may be more receptive to professional than religious influences in their work, the unifying tendencies of medicine tend to override religious differences in the hospitals where doctors work. Medical travelers often note differences in the ways that hospital doctors perform the same acts in different countries, but these seem due to differences in wealth or scientific tradition more often than to religion. Thoracic surgeons in the El-Mieuri General Surgical Hospital of Alexandria seem to do their work in the same way as their teachers in the hospitals of London, and the fact that the former are Muslims and Copts while the latter are Anglicans seems to play no role. Perhaps there are some subtle cross-national differences in the behavior of doctors due to their religious values, but careful research would be needed to discover them.

Nursing service. Since nurses and auxiliaries provide personal service to patients, since they are not conditioned by such a strongly rooted international set of modern techniques and professional values as are doctors, and since they come from lower social classes than do doctors, their work seems more influenced by international differences in religion. Several Western doctors and nurses who have worked or taught in the Muslim and Asian countries told me that the nurses and auxiliaries seem to share some of the public's belief that illness and death are due to God's will and are unavoidable. Western medicine emphasizes special vigilance about the symptoms of the seriously ill and emergency efforts by many people are redoubled when patients become critical, but such action seems to depend on the Christian belief that illness is curable without antagonizing God and that the approach of death is reversible. Several Western nurses teaching or directing Muslim nurses and auxiliaries have told me of the difficulties in inducing these employees to maintain an alert interest in seriously ill patients and in motivating them to act during crises. For example:

There was the case I remember of the patient found dead in bed. He was receiving oxygen in the position at a 90 degree angle. He had been dead for some time with the tube in his nose. There was no dial on the tank. The nasal catheter was in his nose, but no oxygen had been going through. It was felt among the nurses that the patient would have died anyway, that neglecting him had not been so serious.

Such fatalism may be particularly great in pediatric services, since Middle Eastern and Asian folk beliefs assume that Allah's wrath or the Evil Eye falls heavily on babies and children.[72] A Western nursing instructor told some of her observations in a Middle Eastern pediatric hospital:

> The mothers are admitted along with their sick children. The first mother I met was in bed with her child and was very white. She said she had had seven children. The six previous ones had died of malnutrition at two months, and this one was also suffering from malnutrition. Everyone seemed to think little could be done.
>
> Nurses in this pediatric hospital were also apathetic about foundlings. There are many foundlings in the hospital. I saw one room with twenty to twenty-four of them. There was no nurse caring for them, they were not adequately clothed, they lacked shoes, they were dirty. There were only three or four beds in this room, so four to five sick children were in one bed. Orphans and foundlings are not adopted in this country. . . . The hospital normally tries to conceal these children. . . . I felt this resignation that we talked about more in the Children's Hospital than anywhere else.

Because of the Christian principles of self-sacrifice and rewards in the afterlife, Christians may be more tolerant of difficult working conditions. In her sample of Indian nurses, King found that Hindus and Muslims complained about working conditions more often than Christians.[73]

Are there differences between Protestant and Catholic countries resulting from the effects of religion on secular nurses? Nursing for many centuries was a Catholic vocation, and possibly the new technical and professional themes are more congenial to Protestant thinking, while traditional bedside nursing is more congenial to a Catholic or fundamentalist Protestant viewpoint. Or perhaps a more general religious-secular dichotomy underlies these two strands in contemporary nursing. Evidence of the religious-secular division comes from McPartland's content analysis of the bulletins of various American graduate nursing schools.[74] He finds that the religious institutions emphasize the nurse's patient care and humanitarian functions, while the nonsectarian schools encourage professional, technical, and administrative aspirations. Religious and nonsectarian schools recruit students who enter with the corresponding philosophies of nursing, according to McPartland's questionnaire data, but the differences diminish during their education. Deutscher finds traces of this initial difference among American practicing nurses: belief in the importance of formal education and technical training is considered more important among alumnae of nonsectarian schools than among graduates of Catholic schools, with the alumnae of Protestant institutions falling in-between.[75]

Performance of Religious Employees

Organization of work. The community of nuns working at a hospital is led by a Mother Superior who governs the members' lives and who acts as administrative representative of the order. The central office of the order is supreme. Assisting the community Superior is a member who acts as matron over the hospital work of the religious.

Until the Renaissance, ecclesiastic and hospital hierarchies coincided, thus religious and medical responsibilities could not conflict. But the secularization of the hospital introduced lay professionals whose authority derives from technical criteria, first the doctor and later the graduate nurse. Hospitals with religious employees have subtle problems of combining the ecclesiastic and medical hierarchies. As a mystical Bride of Christ and a functionary in His holy Church, the nun possesses a charisma that no layman can rival. She is permitted to live and work only under the authority of the Church; therefore in public hospitals nuns occupy only supervisory jobs and are never subordinates of lay nurses. They are ward sisters and supervisors of the operating room, laboratories, kitchen, etc. In the hospital, only the doctors' medical charisma can match their religious charisma, and therefore—significantly, at the direction of their Church superiors—the service chiefs are the only laymen whose superior authority the nuns recognize in any sphere. In religious hospitals, some nuns work as staff nurses and as nursing students under the authority of other nuns. The nuns' religious charisma produces unusual administrative relationships with doctors and lay professional nurses, both in public and religious hospitals (see pp. 56–60). Since Protestant Deaconesses are not functionaries of a Church with a hierarchical organization and a divine character—significantly, they retain their given and family names—they often have worked in public hospitals under the supervision of lay ward sisters and lay matrons, although probably their subordination was not as strict as would be true of lay staff nurses.

The daily schedule of a nursing religious includes very long hours of work interspersed with brief periods for prayers, meals, and rest.[76] For example, the Community of the Daughters of Charity of St. Vincent de Paul at one of the hospitals in Italy follows this schedule six days a week:

5 A.M.	Wake up.
5 to 5:30 A.M.	Individual meditation.
5:30 to 6 A.M.	Mass in chapel.
6 to 6:30 A.M.	Thanksgiving and breakfast in the refectory.
6:30 to 7 A.M.	Some wash and make up their beds. Some go to the operating rooms or to their wards at 6:30 A.M.
7 A.M. to 12:30 P.M. or later	Work in the hospital.
12:30 to 2:30 P.M.	Lunch and rest.
2:30 to 3 P.M.	Meditation in the chapel.
3 to 9:30 or 10:00 P.M.	Work in the hospital.
9:30 to 10 P.M.	Benediction in the chapel.
10 to 10:30 P.M. or later	Supper.
10:30 to 11 P.M.	Recreation, mostly conversation among the nuns. Sometimes walking in the garden, playing music, watching television.

This schedule varies among countries according to certain national habits. Italians generally have a long lunch hour, and so do Italian nursing nuns; St. Vincent de Paul nuns in Germany, for example, have the shorter German lunch hour, an earlier supper, and a period of work after supper. Total work hours for all nurses vary among countries: Spanish nurses generally once worked longer hours than Italian nurses, and Spanish Daughters of Charity still seem to work longer hours than the Italian Daughters. Within each country, nursing orders vary in the amount of time devoted to chapel prayers, private meditation, and rest. Compared to nuns,

Deaconesses may work fewer hours, spend less time in formal prayer, and spend more time at meals, which in many Deaconess communities are accompanied by prayers and hymn-singing.

Performance. The motivations of performance for a religious are different from those of any lay nurse, because she is primarily a religious. For her, nursing is a means. The pastor of an organization of Protestant Deaconesses writes:

> One still frequently meets people who imagine that a Deaconess is before all a nurse. They see in her a nurse of a certain quality: she is good, she gives all her time to her patients, she remains a long time in the hospital or home where she is located, and she does not cost too much. . . . The Deaconess is not at all the woman of whom we have just spoken. She has taken seriously the call which Christ has addressed to her and each day she tries to respond always better to the demands of this call. Her vocation is not a fancy of her nature, nor a wish to be happy by addicting herself to a propensity of her physical being. Her vocation is the expression of the will of God who has decided that this woman would be a Deaconess, i.e., his servant to alleviate the miseries of human suffering, and also for the preparation of the Kingdom of God. Thereby the Deaconess bears witness by all her life and by the entire length of her existence that God exists, that he speaks, that he orders, that he has a plan for each of us and for all humanity, that he governs his creation and that he will crown his work by the appearance of his Kingdom. . . .
>
> Her professional activity is the framework in which she exercises her mission.[77]

A laywoman can perform her nursing roles in different ways according to her psychological needs and the religious will perform their apostolic roles in different ways according to their theological philosophies and individual personalities.[78] One might approach nursing work as a personal penance, another might interpret it as an opportunity for glorifying God and saving souls through maximum productivity. Possibly one tendency is developed more than the other if one compares denominations, entire societies, or individual religious orders. For example, the culture of a country like America may encourage the go-getting rather than the penitential approach to the apostolate; therefore America may produce different kinds of recruits and train and control them differently, in contrast to comparable orders of certain other countries. This subtle interplay between religious socialization and the mode of performing apostolic work is still unstudied; doubtless there are cross-national differences even in a Church whose international organization tends to minimize them.

How do religious compare with lay nurses doing the same tasks? First of all, do religious give priority to religious duties over nursing, in contrast to the professional nurses' behavior? In theory, no contradiction should occur. The nursing nun and Deaconess serve God by serving suffering humans, and therefore they should perform both spiritual and clinical duties well.

However, conflicts and debatable priorities may have occurred in the past. Because the religious are concerned with the spiritual as well as physical health of the patient, the nun and Deaconess have always believed that spiritual experiences should be readily available. Before the modernization of medical care and of hospital organizations, the religious were not taught about urgent clinical procedures, they had not learned the technical and affectively neutral attitudes toward illnesses and patients that characterize modern professional nursing. In those years, for example, the religious in emergencies might notify the priest before the doctor, they might encourage ill patients to perform the usual Friday fasting, or they might allow patients on bed-rest to get up and pray in the ward and chapel.[79] Nuns in Paris and perhaps elsewhere refused to care for venereal disease patients.[80]

However, the medical functions of the hospital have become more salient during modernization, the professional nursing training of religious has improved, and ecclesiastical Superiors now emphasize that religious must do their hospital jobs well.[81] Thus the difference in job definitions and priorities between religious and lay nurses has probably diminished in all countries. The visitor sometimes hears anticlerical doctors and lay nurses in some of the Latin European countries grumble that some nuns still give their religious interests priority over their nursing duties in ways common in previous centuries—for example, by calling the priest to the bedside before the doctor, by leaving the ward unattended while they go to chapel, or by giving devout patients the best service—but considerable impartial research would be needed to discover whether, where, and why such acts occur.

Since the Church defines nursing as a means of serving Christ, nuns are taught to give priority to medical emergencies over postponable rituals. During my visits to European hospitals, nuns often gave priority to their medical duties—or even to interviews with a visiting sociologist—during the time when the rest of the community was in chapel. Because some nuns are always doing urgent work or have special assignments, such as night duty, an entire community is rarely in the chapel at the same time.

As medical care and hospitals modernized, so did the nursing orders.[82] Many communities postponed their times for rising in the morning—for example, from 4 A.M. to 5 A.M. today in many Italian hospitals—so they would not tire from the more rapid work tempo. The Daughters of Charity of St. Vincent de Paul streamlined their famous bonnets and their full gowns, so they could move about the wards and laboratories more easily. Adjustments between hospitals and orders have been mutual. In hospitals where nuns and Deaconesses have worked for centuries, medical routines have developed in such a way as to avoid conflict with religious obligations. For example, when surgery grew, operating room schedules evolved that would fall between the religious' early morning and noon prayers.

Probably, the religious perform better than the lay nurse certain religious tasks that both should do, such as calling a priest for a patient in need or providing the patient with religious information. In certain countries with widespread anticlericalism—possibly France—religious nurses might do such acts far more conscientiously than laywomen.

Are there any differences in how religious and lay nurses perform the same medical and administrative acts? This depends on the level of nursing and prenursing education the religious receive in a country. In many countries once and in some orders in some countries today, novices have had only some primary education in parochial school before entering the convent. Also, until recently, religious learned nursing by assisting older practitioners rather than by getting formal instruction. Leaders of apostolic orders are very sensitive to lay accusations of professional deficiency,[83] and they have attempted to modernize standards. In many countries recently, educational prerequisites for novices have risen. Catholic and Protestant Churches insist that religious perform their worldly tasks with the same skill as laywomen,[84] nursing licensure laws in many countries apply to religious as well as to laywomen, and therefore all new religious nurses now graduate from graduate nursing schools run by their orders. In some countries like Holland, such schools have existed for decades, and it is widely believed that religious and lay nurses do not differ materially in professional skills. In other countries, such as Spain, the schools for religious are new, many religious nurses have no formal training, the average nun has less prenursing education than the average professional nurse, and many observers believe that discrepancies in skills are often substantial—with, of course, the exception of some well-trained nuns. The discrepancies in performance are the expected results of inadequate education. For example, a Spanish doctor compared nuns and professional nurses in language echoed by many other medical informants in Latin Europe:

> Nuns are usually less exact in measuring doses. They are less exact in accounting for time, that is, they are less careful in giving injections exactly on time. They may be less conscientious or practiced in sterile technique. They may be less expert in arranging materials, such as arranging instruments or medications for giving treatments. They are less likely to realize that medicine changes, they keep up with newest things less. This is a problem, because many nuns are older; there are few old lay women practicing nursing. I remember one nun who had been a nurse when my father—later professor of medicine—was a medical student. I was doing something according to the newest technical procedures, and she asked me, "Why don't you do it the simpler way, as your father did, and not this complicated way?"...
>
> They follow doctors' orders about bed rest. If anything, they are more strict about bed rest. Nuns are fussy over the cleanliness of the wards. Sometimes if a patient goes about and smokes, nuns may ask us to put him on bed rest.

Nursing nuns may perform some medical and administrative tasks differently from lay nurses because of their religious attitudes and religious training. For example, in most (but not all) countries, they may avoid catheterizing and bathing patients and leave this to the lay nurses or auxiliaries. In the hospitals that I visited, the nuns seemed stricter than lay head nurses when running pediatric services; in some countries, the nuns more often put boys and girls in separate wards. In the countries experimenting with open-door psychiatric care, such as England and Holland, the nuns seem more hesitant to unlock doors than are lay nurses. Compared to lay head nurses, nuns seem even more concerned with keeping rooms clean and keeping equipment, instruments, and supplies neatly arranged.

Effects on structure: relations with doctors. Social change has laicized public hospitals, and injected into the organization a layman pre-eminent according to the hospital's new values, namely the doctor. Relations between religious and doctor are fundamentally different from those between lay professional nurse and doctor; the religious has her own charisma according to a supernatural frame of reference and according to religious organizations, and the apostolic sphere in which she works with the doctor is secondary to her religious obligations. Complications arise if the individual doctor and the hospital setting emphasize the professional criteria and dismiss the religious frame of reference.[85]

Relations between doctor and religious are not the same in sectarian and public hospitals, since the sectarian organization is part of a structure defining her as his superior. Although their daily contacts are conducted in her apostolic and his medical spheres, where he is conceded higher authority, her special connection with the hospital ownership is never forgotten. "We must always remember," a chief of service in a European Deaconess hospital said, "we are not the owners, we are only guests. It is their house. When policy questions arise, we must convince them." Relations between religious and doctors seem harmonious also because of the self-selection of the doctors. They are usually members of that faith, and if they had not been favorable to religious, they would not have joined such a hospital.

Relations between nuns and many doctors in public hospitals seem to a visitor very amicable on the surface, particularly in the countries with the least anticlericalism. In strongly Catholic societies, nuns are met repeatedly in everyday life, many people have relatives in orders, and therefore most come to take the presence of nuns for granted. The visitor notices much warmth and joking between nuns and many doctors. Many doctors are pleased by the polite respect of the nuns; in many Latin countries the nuns fuss over their favorite doctors and give parties on the latter's Name Days. An Italian doctor explained why he prefers nuns to professional nurses:

> If you tell nuns do twenty-five things on a list, they do it in that order. A professional nurse would do it more flexibly and would question. . . . I prefer nuns because they are more serious in their work than professional nurses. . . . Nuns are best, since you don't have to discuss with them. Just tell them what to do and they do it.

Although nuns seem serenely benevolent toward all and tell the interviewer that no one dislikes them, some public hospital doctors —particularly young men in countries with much anticlericalism— prefer lay professional nurses. Many doctors complain to an interviewer that the nuns, particularly the older ones without formal schooling, lack the technical skills of professional lay nurses. Some doctors say they can control the lay nurses more easily than religious. In the public hospitals that I visited, a common pattern is that the doctors ask rather than simply order the religious, almost never rebuke her, and avoid profanity in her presence; with the lay nurse they are more at ease but also more authoritarian. Authority relations are particularly different at lower ranks of medical staffs; in most of the world any hospital doctor can give an order to any nurse in his service, but often nuns—in conformity with the hierarchical customs of the Church and with an awareness of their own special status—will take orders only from the chief of service, will follow orders of subordinate doctors only if the orders are approved by the chief, and may ignore the demands of younger doctors who render them insufficient respect. Sample surveys would be needed before one can estimate whether most doctors are friendly or unfriendly, and the circumstances governing relationships. Possibly surgeons are more critical of nuns than are internists, because of differences in the social organization of the fields: surgery demands the highest technical expertise from all members of the surgical team, it requires more subordination and obedience to the doctor, and its work pace is faster.

Some hostile chiefs of service—particularly in Italian and French cities—have attempted to bypass the religious and work with lay professional nurses. Head-on tests of strength are usually avoided but sometimes occur; for example, occasionally Italian professors have invoked the full power of their respected position and have used threats of resignation to force the hospital to replace all nuns on their service with lay professional nurses. (Nuns would continue to work on other services.) More often, the nuns agree to a division of labor. Throughout Latin Europe, the religious are relinquishing actual surgical nursing to the lay graduate nurses, even while remaining as head theater nurse and chief administrator. In many Spanish hospitals, such division of labor is extended to all services; the religious are head nurses and do all the administration and ward housekeeping, but lay graduate nurses handle or supervise all medications, dressings, and medical work. In many public hospitals, the community Superior has decided to withdraw nuns from the technical departments of the hospital, such as the laboratories, emergency room, and X-ray, and to concentrate them in services where a spiritual atmosphere and personal contact are considered important, such as obstetrics, pediatrics, and internal medicine.

Effects on structure: relations with lay graduate nurses. Modernization has injected lay graduate nurses into the modern hospital but has not yet given them the same expertise and charisma with which lay doctors have gained the deference of the religious. Instead of performing an independent and new function, the laywoman is simply taking over the field once monopolized by the religious, a natural situation for invidious comparisons and conflicts of authority.

Apparently, relationships are harmonious in the multireligion countries such as Holland and America. There religious nurses work only in religious hospitals, and the graduate nurses in these hospitals are usually communicants who have attended religious nursing schools and who respect and like nuns. But a very different situation exists in the Catholic countries.[86] There nuns work in public hospitals, in association with lay graduate nurses who for the most part attended secular schools. The two groups have different ambitions, different work schedules, and often different philosophies of nursing. Paradoxically, lay graduate nursing is the reference group of the religious leaders who are now trying to modernize the nursing performance of nuns, but perhaps the average nun rarely thinks of individual lay nurses as her peers in any way.

The lay graduate nurses in public and even in religious hospitals were the only group that nuns disparaged during my interviews.

Repeatedly they compared the laywomen's motivations and performance unfavorably with their own. For example:

> A worldly nurse is in the hospital for a different purpose. For her it is a job, and she avoids those tasks which are not part of the job as she sees it. A nun would not consider anything outside her responsibility or contract. There are worldly nurses who are good Christians; and they may do the same things as the nun with a sense of service. But she would not have the same degree of dedication as a sister, who serves because of her religion and dedicates herself totally.

When asked to compare the performance of religious and lay nurses, nuns repeatedly told me—often with considerable asperity —that the laywomen worked eight hours a day, went home to their families, and left the nuns to care for the patients the rest of the time. Whenever I asked nuns to describe the schedule of the lay nurses in their hospitals, they always underestimated the amount of working time the laywomen actually spent, according to the hospital records that I subsequently checked.

Lay graduate nurses are a new group in the Latin countries; they harbor considerable resentment about the entrenched position of nuns, who always occupy head nurse jobs and therefore block the advancement of the laywomen. The lay nurses have other complaints too, such as the following from one Italian informant:

> Their position is very good. If we make a mistake, we pay. We may be transferred to another job. We will be rebuked, a note will be entered in our records. But if a nun makes a mistake, nothing happens to her. No one rebukes or transfers her. Nuns are always in charge. Some lack enough nursing education, are old-fashioned and stupid. So some of us are assigned as helpers to such nuns, when we have more education, and resentment results. . . . Nuns never work on night duty, since they are always chief nurses or assistant chief nurses.

Lay nurses' resentment of nuns seems greatest in the most anticlerical countries, such as France and Italy; it will probably grow in Spain, as the number of lay graduate nurses increases and as the country becomes more secular. Although personal conflicts exist, doubtless amicable nurse-nun pairs exist too, just as in the relations between doctors and religious.

In some countries, policy conflicts have developed between the national representatives of the religious and lay nurses. In the past, religious worked long hours, received minimum pocket money from their orders, and did all sorts of domestic work and personal care in the wards. Some of their leaders still think of nursing as this kind of total dedication with performance of any sort of work— even though in practice most religious now work as head nurses and delegate the more menial tasks to lay auxiliaries.[87] The leaders of the religious in the Latin countries and in Germany have been consistently reluctant to join with the lay graduate leaders in demanding better wages, shorter hours, and more professional job definitions for the lay nurses, partly because such changes would contradict the religious' conception of the true nature of nursing and partly because such changes would raise the costs of the sectarian hospitals. Since the religious leaders speak not only for their own members but in some countries also for the lay graduate nurses trained in their schools, their reluctance weakens the power of the lay graduate leaders when bargaining with governments and other hospital owners. This conflict may diminish in the future, if the Church continues to modernize its apostolic work with lay professional nursing as its reference group. In Holland, Italy, America, and elsewhere, religious and lay leaders already collaborate in the development of nursing curricula and of other professional standards. But competition for head nursing jobs in hospitals will remain troublesome for a long time.

Medical Policy

Certain fundamental life processes are central questions for both religion and medicine, and it is these areas that become the subjects of hospital policy most influenced by religion. Natural events are deemed manifestations of a guiding supernatural reality, and acts or objects are classified as "sacred" and "profane." Religious persons aspire with great intensity to participate in supernatural realms by honoring sacred objects, obeying sacred rituals, and avoiding the profane. There is a constant danger of exclusion resulting from neglect or violation. Certain stages in life cannot be negotiated without rites of passage, and the individual insists on their observance both for himself and his relatives.[88] Since hospitals deal with birth, death, sexuality, nutrition, and other activities of sacred significance to a religion, they are pressed to conform to the religion's observances. If the hospitals carry out the denomination's rules, its power in society will remain undiminished: the hospitals will be executing the procedures previously performed by the family and by the clergy. But if the hospitals ignore the denomination's prescriptions, important areas of social life will be desacralized, and the denomination will lose followers. Medical policy in public hospitals often is disputed among the denominations with rival definitions of the sacred and profane. Secular groups—usually including the doctors and hospital administrators—often feud with all denominations, if the latter demand special facilities or procedures that divert resources or alter procedures from their own purely technical "modern" standard.

Birth. The beginning of individual life is specially significant in nearly every religion, and many faiths prescribe taboos or obligations about conception and birth. Human life is believed holy. The newborn must be protected against destruction and suffering and therefore must be initiated into the sacred community.

Both Christianity and Judaism argue that destruction of life is an offense against God, that the foetus has a soul at some point after conception, and that destruction of the foetus is wrong. The conditions under which a foetus may be destroyed depend on the religion's conception of the starting time of life and the priorities given to the welfare of the mother and of the foetus. After a lengthy theological debate, the Catholic Church in the Middle Ages abandoned Aristotle's theory that the foetus "quickened" and began to live on the fortieth day after conception, and the Church held that the foetal life began at conception. As a result, the Church and a few other conservative Christian denominations would allow abortions only in exceptional circumstances, such as the incidental result of surgery that was not intended only to eliminate the foetus but was aimed at some other medical problem. Orthodox Judaism retained Aristotle's distinction and therefore its traditional law forbade abortion after the fortieth day. Any threat to the mother's life, however, would make abortion not merely permissible but obligatory. Some wholly secular or "materialist" positions would allow (although not encourage) abortion as a birth control technique requested by the patient like any other kind of elective surgery. Some religions, such as Orthodox Christianity and Islam, believe that life begins at birth; they do not explicitly forbid abortions; but they consider birth and production of new life as particularly important to God, and some of their interpreters condemn abortion and birth control.[89]

Because of the range among countries in theological principle, Church influence, and nonreligious pressures, official laws and the policies of public hospitals vary widely.[90] Possibly countries having abortion policies can be arranged roughly according to their religious conservatism, where "conservatism" refers to a set of ideas and practices that may correlate—namely, a belief in the existence of souls under God's protection, the imputation of souls to the unborn and dead, the devaluation of scientific as compared to religious judgments in questions of life and death, and the devaluation of doctors in comparison to priests. In all countries with firmly planted and conservative religious beliefs—whether strongly Catholic like Eire and Spain, or mixed Catholic and Calvinist like Holland, or Muslim—the public hospitals do not perform direct intentional abortions for any reason. In Catholic countries where the Church influence is restricted by anticlericalism (such as Italy and France), in Orthodox Greece, and in the more conservative Protestant countries (such as England formerly) pregnancies can be interrupted in the public hospital if a committee of doctors believes the mother's life is endangered; a formal administrative procedure must be used to get permission and to assign a gynecologist. In the less conservative Protestant countries such as Sweden, Iceland, and England after 1967, a pregnancy can be interrupted in the public hospital if a committee of doctors believes that the birth might harm the mother's mental health or personal welfare. In countries with antireligious governments (such as Eastern Europe) or in countries whose national religions do not imply that conception and birth have supernatural aspects (such as Japan), abortions can be performed in the public hospitals for justifiable birth control purposes, although hospital policy may try to discourage applicants by requiring counselling or by charging fees. Policies may change when the strength of religious influence varies. For example, the extremely proclerical Vichy government of France, motivated partly by the Church and partly by the racist views of its own civil leaders, adopted drastic laws against all abortions; but after the Liberation, Church and State were again separated and the prewar laws were restored.[91]

So much for official policy; how religion relates to actual practice is a distinct question. Policy is determined in large part by Church influence over the government; practice is determined by the strength and specific content of religious attitudes in the population and in the health professions. Sometimes the discrepancy is great. For example the proclerical conservative parties of France, acting under the influence of the Church and of nationalists worried about depopulation, have kept in effect some of the world's most stringent laws against abortion. But many Frenchmen are apathetic toward religion and hostile to the Church; they, and even many religious people, give priority to their personal problems over religious doctrine; and as a result France has long had many illegal nontherapeutic abortions in private clinics and in the private offices of doctors and midwives. Church influence on policy may have unintentionally increased the amount of abortion in practice, because French laws, until 1967, prevented the spread of contraceptive clinics and effective contraceptive methods.

Abortions are occasions for the interplay of religious principle, public policy, professional ethics, and the doctor's personal self-interest. Under some conditions they converge, under other conditions there are differences and conflicts, sometimes presenting dilemmas for the doctor and hospital administrator. Holland is an example of convergence resulting in few abortions—the principal Churches oppose the performance of abortions for therapeutic or elective reasons; government officials, the public, and medical functionaries reveal a strong moral sense in their conversation and behavior; the public likes large families; doctors experience no financial pressure to deviate from professional or public ethics; and therefore the ban on hospital and private abortions is thought to be observed remarkably well. Japan is an example of convergence resulting in many abortions—the country's principal religions, laws, and codes of professional ethics are very permissive; doctors and midwives believe they are badly paid for other medical acts by the insurance funds and by private patients; thus Japan has many abortions.[92]

Sometimes the religious, public, and professional policies agree, but some doctors lapse. For example, in Spain and Italy elective abortions are considered immoral and illegal by the Church, State, and Medical Association, but the surplus of doctors and the desperate competition for patients tempt some to perform abortions. The Medical Associations face a grave dilemma, since they would be supporting an unpopular Church and an unpopular State against their members, but there is enough cynicism about official morality in both countries to provide rationalizations for lax enforcement of professional ethics. Sometimes Church and State disagree, and doctors and hospitals are torn. For example, in Poland during the 1960s, the government authorized public hospitals to perform abortions as a means of birth control; the Cardinal condemned this in a pastoral letter read from all pulpits. Since the Medical Association avoids conflicts with the government, there is no independent professional body to guide the hospital doctors. The regime allowed the doctors to make their own decisions, and many have refused to participate in caring for such patients, partly because of their personal religious conscience, partly as a quiet protest against the government, and partly to avoid involvement in the unpredictable Church-State conflict.

Religion affects hospital obstetric procedures in other ways too. Many popular interpretations of religions have emphasized female modesty and therefore have insisted that mothers can be delivered by midwives rather than by men. Since such societies assume that childbirth is a normal function rather than a medical problem, they do not perceive a need to involve a doctor, who is likely to be a man.[93] These were widespread folk Christian beliefs for many centuries, and only recently has normal hospital delivery by obstetricians become common in Europe and the Anglo-Saxon countries. Resistance remains strong in Islam because of the *Koran's* (XXIV:31) injunction to women "to lower their gaze and be modest, and to display of their adornment only that which is apparent, and to draw their veils over their bosoms, and not to reveal their adornment save to their own" immediate family and servants. As a result, there is much less hospital delivery in Muslim than in Christian countries. (Even the one Christian country that still retains a strong tradition of home delivery, namely Holland, probably has a higher rate of hospital delivery than any Muslim country.) Even though Egypt has a much higher birth rate than the West, its much lower rate of hospital delivery means that it has fewer obstetrical cases among hospital admissions than does the West, namely ll percent in comparison with about 15 percent in America.[94] In some Muslim countries, hospital antenatal clinics must be conducted almost secretly because customarily women do not travel around publicly.[95] When some conservative Muslim countries request a maternal and child health consultant from international organizations, they specify that it be a woman. In order to encourage hospital deliveries, some medical schools in underdeveloped countries now reserve space for female medical students, so that obstetrics and gynecology will become a female specialty.[96] Modernization displaces traditional folk beliefs first among many upper class urban Muslims, and thus one finds some private obstetrical clinics in Middle Eastern cities where male doctors perform the deliveries. For example, of the one hundred hospitals in Lebanon during the early 1960s, eighteen were private obstetrical clinics and many of the others were general private clinics with obstetrical services.

Most religions initiate the newborn into the sect by certain rites, and sometimes they must be done during the time when the baby is still in the hospital. So the hospital must provide facilities. For example, in every Christian country hospitals have arrangements and sites for baptizing the baby, if this must be done before discharge and before the family can go to its customary church. All Israeli hospitals and all Jewish hospitals elsewhere have special rooms for the family to witness the ritual circumcision of the newborn boy and then to take the ceremonial dinner.[97] Colorful baptism ceremonies are regularly conducted by Orthodox priests on Greek and Cypriote maternity wards.

Several folk religions attribute special significance to the placenta, which Christianity and Judaism treat as disposable waste. Certain rituals are performed with the placenta and it is buried ceremonially, in order to ensure the safety of child and mother. Magical properties may be attributed to the placenta, and if the omens are dangerous, ceremonial exorcisms must be performed or the baby must be killed. In much of Africa, hospitals must be prepared to deliver the placenta to the family, or mothers will not agree to delivery there. Nurses and obstetricians must know the ceremonially "right" information to give to the family about the character of the placenta, or the baby might be killed.[98]

Death. Some of the most crucial social functions of religion are to define the meaning of death, propitiate the forces that cause death, predict the destination of the dead, and—in death-denying religions—confer upon the survivors ritual tasks that convey a feeling that they have helped the deceased on his journey and that the society will do the same for them. Because the death of others and of one's own self generates so much anxiety, religious theories are elaborate, and rituals are detailed and often inflexible. Social disapproval of violations of doctrine and ritual is extreme, for it may be believed that the spirit of the dead will suffer or that the spirit world will penalize the survivors. Some religions which deny that physical death terminates the life of the individual require the preservation of the body or require certain treatment of the body, as conditions for the spirit's survival or for the achievement of its desired destination. Some religions that accept death as final for both body and spirit believe that disposal of the body according to prescribed procedures is essential to protect survivors from disharmonies in the natural or supernatural realms. As the society modernizes, its population becomes less concerned with the effects of death upon the happiness and stability of survivors, and more interested in how knowledge about the causes of death can prolong natural life.[99]

Since the hospital deals with the dying and dead, it enters one of the most sensitive areas of religious doctrine and church responsibility. Problems arise in non-Western societies. Since the modern hospital evolved in a Christian environment, its customs and functional needs became adjusted to the Christian approach to death. The modern hospital is based on the procedures and knowledge derived from the secularization of attitudes toward death in Christian societies; it is based on modern scientific investigation into the causes and postponement of death. Exported to non-Christian societies, the Western-style hospital routines sometimes contradict still deeply rooted religious norms about the treatment of the dying and dead. To insist on running the hospital in Western ways is to risk a fatal war with powerful opponents who have won other battles, namely public opinion and the clergy. Therefore, in practice hospitals must adjust.

Christianity has never developed special taboos about the place of death for various reasons: since it is concerned primarily with the relations between the living person and God in preparation for the afterlife, it treats the moment of death more incidentally than do some other religions; since it makes a fundamental distinction between the soul and body, and since the body is temporary and secondary, the place where the body dies is not a central religious question. Instead of developing an elaborate doctrine about the appropriate place of death, the various Christian denominations simply say that the dying person should be put anywhere that is comfortable and where clergy will be available for whatever ceremonies they require. (Catholicism, of course, insists on confession and the last rites when possible.) So the hospital is an appropriate place for death; in fact, for centuries Western hospitals were organized as places for the dying.

However, where non-Western religions attach special significance to the place of death, hospitals must avoid allowing patients to die within their walls or must avoid publicity about deaths. For example, some African religions believe that the moment of death is a magical event, that new corpses are dangerous, and that any building where someone has died is accursed. So the hospital must put dying patients outdoors or in disposable huts, lest patients and employees refuse to enter the main building in the future. Some African religions believe the person must die in his home village amidst local rituals, or his soul will become lost. So hospitals must send dying patients back to the family, a policy that has the advantage of avoiding the unfavorable public image that would result from an excessive mortality rate.

Modern scientific medicine and medical education depend on autopsies. Popular thinking in many societies is repelled by the idea of dissection, particularly of relatives, even when the religion lacks specific doctrines excluding it. For example, although Confucianism does not foresee an afterlife, it does reinforce traditional China's respect for ancestors, and this has long been enough to keep Chinese hospital autopsy rates very low.

Christianity's distinction between soul and body is one of the few doctrines in any religion that can be interpreted as allowing autopsies. The soul is separate from the flesh and blood; the body is "of dust" and will eventually dissolve. After baptism, the body is "a temple of God" which should be treated with respect and be given the ritual of "Christian burial." But it is the soul that is the responsible agent: the soul has followed (or ignored) divine teachings, it survives after the death of the body, it waits for a while, and then it achieves resurrection when God approves. The soul, although immortal, in death escapes from its corporeal form; when God resurrects a soul, its form will be renewed.[100]

For centuries some Church leaders denounced the excessive and unregulated practice of dissection and threatened penalties against those acting without Church permission. Some extreme critics within the Church claimed dissection was completely forbidden on religious grounds, but the Church never took an official position, except to deplore disrespect to corpses, and occasional autopsies occurred with or without ecclesiastical permission before the Renaissance. One reason for the criticisms of post-mortems was that some of the churchmen were only echoing public bias against autopsies. Another reason was that the Church had become involved in medical politics; it had come to support Galen's theories against the school of Vesalius, and thus it opposed the latter's research techniques.[101] But the aforementioned doctrines about soul and body were available for an adjustment of Church policy: because the body deserved respect but was not sacrosanct, it could be used to promote the common good. Two of the breakthrough periods in Western medicine were the Italian Renaissance and the nineteenth century in Paris, when anatomists and physiologists performed autopsies with the tolerance and occasionally even the cooperation of the Catholic Church. By distinguishing between body and soul in the salvation process and by giving different values to body and soul, Christianity is nearly unique among the world's religions. And that is why the teaching hospitals of Europe and of the Western Hemisphere are virtually the only ones in the world with numerous autopsies.

Several religions believe that *both* body and soul will live on in the next world, and therefore the body must be complete at burial. The detailed Muslim burial customs, specified in post-Koranic exegeses, require that the entire body—including, if possible, parts amputated years before[102]—shall be buried in a particular position facing Mecca. Burial within twenty-four hours is urgent, since the soul leaves the body when it becomes cold and since the body becomes alive again when it is interred. Two persons of the same sex as the deceased wash his body ceremonially and dress him in a white shroud.[103] The urgency of the burial makes a leisurely hospital autopsy impossible. A dissected body would repel the family and would jeopardize the resurrection of the person, particularly if organs had been removed for laboratory examinations.

Without specific Koranic bases, some Muslim denominations have evolved theories about postburial events that would be hampered by dissection. For the first hours, the soul and body sleep together. That night, two angels temporarily rouse body and soul back to life again and question the person about his belief in Allah. If the answers are satisfactory, the angels bid body and soul sleep again. Souls then leave the body to live in a heavenly place until Judgment Day, when soul and body are again reunited either in Paradise or in Hades.[104]

Arab medical science and medical education, even during their most productive periods,[105] have always been handicapped by a shortage of post-mortems. Attempts to dissect bodies have aroused protests by *ulemas*, riots, and occasional assassination attempts against the dissectors.[106] Fear of autopsies may always have kept some patients away from hospitals. Today few autopsies are performed in Muslim countries. Some of the more conservative ones, such as Afghanistan, have laws forbidding them. In most Muslim countries, certainty of refusal by the family precludes officials and doctors from requesting or attempting post-mortems for scientific reasons.[107] Only in a few of the less religious areas, such as Ankara and Istanbul, can the teaching hospitals dissect as many as half the deaths.

The Muslim taboo against autopsies produces dilemmas when a Middle Eastern hospital tries to emulate a European scientific and educational standard. For example, a few years ago one such hospital was accredited for undergraduate and postgraduate training by the American Medical Association and the American Hospital Association; at that time, the desire for accreditation had raised the autopsy rate to 20 percent, considerably lower than American hospitals of its class but accepted by the accrediting authorities in view of the special national conditions. Since then, the post-mortem rate has dropped; during the year of my visit, the pathologist complained there had not been a single adult autopsy. Some of the

American staff members believed the local doctors—both Christian and Muslim—avoided asking permission from the families and avoided raising clinical questions that might necessitate dissection.

In contrast to Christianity, the Old Testament implies that the human body has a special divine character, and the Talmud prescribes detailed burial procedures. God made man in His own image,[108] and therefore man must respect all bodies. Man must not alter any body but should preserve it intact for the heavenly life when the Messiah comes. Some Jewish sects, such as the Hassidim, have customarily saved cut hair, cut fingernails, and spilled blood for burial with the rest of the body. Interment must occur within twenty-four hours of death, since the continued presence of a corpse defiles the living. Still unresolved is a centuries-long debate among theologians whether autopsies serve the admittedly higher end of preserving the living and thus whether exceptions could be made to the foregoing rules.[109]

The autopsy issue has been one of Israel's principal medical controversies, because the country now must train its own doctors and because the country's hospitals and growing medical school have aspired to high international rank in teaching and research according to the scientific standards of Christian countries. There had been no problem in the Diaspora; Jewish doctors studied in Gentile medical schools, and Jewish hospitals had few post-mortems. Inclusion of a medical school in the Hebrew University of Jerusalem was delayed for several decades, in large part by rabbinical objection to autopsies. Negotiations between the Chief Rabbinate and the Hadassah Hospital and Medical School resulted in legislation in 1953 allowing autopsies in all medico-legal cases; in scientific or teaching cases when a committee of doctors certifies that the cause of death is unknown and that the lives of similar patients will be assisted; and in cases of voluntary agreement between patient and doctor for teaching purposes, provided the patient has previously agreed in writing. The pathology laboratory must preserve all dissected parts and return them for burial.[110]

Orthodox Israelis have criticized the legislation as inherently contrary to higher religious law. They have accused the hospitals of abuse, by appointing medical committees that will falsely certify the necessity of dissection for clinical knowledge. Some Orthodox families, led by their rabbis, have invaded hospitals and taken away deceased relatives before autopsies could be performed. Control over the Israeli Ministry of Health became a crucial goal of the Orthodox. During the years when the Minister was a member of the militantly secular Mapam party, the Orthodox denounced the hospitals for excessive and unnecessary dissection. When the dominant coalition lost votes in the 1961 election, the Prime Minister turned to the National Religious Front to gain a working majority in the Parliament, and the Front assumed the health portfolio. When Mapam again took over the Ministry in 1966, agitation about autopsies resumed and grew.[111] The dissection controversy has aroused widespread anticlericalism among Israeli doctors.

Food. Food and drink have ritual significance in many religions, and hospitals must conform to the dietary customs of their employees, patients, and governing authorities. A few religions require special styles of food preparation. The most important effect on hospitals is found in Israel, where the kosher requirement of separate preparation of meat and milk products nearly doubles the size and equipment of each hospital kitchen in the country. Israel as a result probably has the largest and costliest hospital kitchens in the world.

Partial and complete fasts are prescribed by many religions. Usually sick people are exempted by some doctrine in each religion,[112] but devout patients may insist on fasting, even against medical advice. The more devout members of hospital staffs—for example, auxiliaries more often than doctors—may fast, with some loss of efficiency. In Muslim countries hospital routine usually slows down during Ramadan, because employees (particularly male auxiliaries, technicians, and porters) fast during the day, spend part of their nights eating, and while at work are often weak, sleepy, irritable, and distracted by thoughts and incessant conversations about food. Many Israelis fast on Yom Kippur, but this is a national holiday lasting only one day a year, and therefore hospital schedules are not disrupted by the letdown of activity. Hospitals in nearly all Catholic countries once served no meat on Fridays, but the population throughout their lifetimes had become accustomed to fish substitutes; indeed, in most of the world beef is a delicacy served rarely at home or in hospitals. Several religions have specific food taboos—no pork for Muslims and Jews, no milk, eggs, or meat for devout Buddhists—but the alternatives are customary in homes and hospitals.[113] It is sometimes difficult to prepare a high-protein diet for devout Buddhists, but substitutes can be found.

Timetables. Most religions designate certain days of the week and certain periods of the year for special observance. Thus in every country, the holy day of the predominant religion is the weekly day of rest of the hospitals. Most of the staff is off duty, the operating rooms and other departments handle only emergencies, and visiting hours are longer than usual. Jewish doctrine goes farther than other religions by forbidding anything but the saving of life on the Sabbath.[114] This produces an even lower level of holy day activity in Israeli than in foreign hospitals, particularly in establishments with very Orthodox employees and patients. The weekly day of rest varies by religion—Sunday in the Christian countries, Friday in the Muslim countries, and Saturday in Israel.

Hospital schedules in Israel are complicated by the Orthodox Jewish prohibition of the use of mechanical devices on the Sabbath. Exceptions are justified in order to save life; thus the Chief Rabbinate has agreed that the hospitals can use electricity, machinery, and marked ambulances on Friday night and Saturday. But a recurring controversy is how to transport employees between their homes and the hospital. Except in Haifa, all public transportation shuts down on the Sabbath, and private cars and taxis move only because they are unofficial and ignore the rabbis. Hospital officials and the Chief Rabbinate have negotiated compromise agreements, allowing the employees to use a few specially marked buses owned by the hospital and allowing doctors to use their private cars only for medical need. However, some zealots are opposed to any vehicular movement, and they may neither know nor care when the driver is a doctor at work. One of Jerusalem's largest hospitals is situated adjacent to the very orthodox Mea Shearim district, and doctors driving to and from work on the Sabbath have sometimes been stoned. Like dissection, the transportation issue has intensified the secular and antisectarian attitudes of many Israeli doctors.

Summary

Each chapter will conclude with a set of propositions that codify my principal findings. Independent variables will be taken from the larger social structure, notably religion, family, and economy. The dependent variables are the chief organizational characteristics of hospitals.

The hospital traits to be used throughout Chapters 2, 3, and 4 were listed at the end of Chapter 1 (pp. 10–11). Following are the principal religious determinants employed in this chapter:

A.1 Religious doctrines that strangers should be helped:
    A.1.1 Extent of acceptance
    A.1.2 Strength of the mandate
A.2 Religious doctrines minimizing supernatural explanations of disease
A.3 Religious doctrines teaching the reversibility of illness by practical human action
A.4 Ecclesiastic organization
A.5 Number of religions in a society
A.6 Functional specificity between religion and medicine

Following are the chief propositions that appeared amidst the substantive detail in this chapter, where the religious variables were determinants and hospital characteristics were the consequences:

The more widely practiced in society are religions that teach help to strangers (A.1.1), then:

The larger the number of persons working in hospitals (1.1.1)
The larger the resources invested in hospitals (1.2 and 1.3)
The greater the consensus over goals of hospital work (4.5)
The more consistent the provision of services according to patients' medical needs rather than personal characteristics (4.3)
The more conscientious the patient care (4.1 and 4.2)

The stronger a religion's mandate to help strangers (A.1.2), then:

The larger the number of persons from that sect in hospital work (1.1.1)
The stronger the spiritual motives for employment (1.1.4)
The greater the donation of resources by that sect (1.2 and 1.3)
The stronger the priority given by employees to hospital work over the demands of other social statuses (4.7)
The longer are working hours (4.9)

The greater the support by the employee's nonmedical social statuses (4.8)

The more extensive are religions teaching that illness is due to natural events (A.2), then:

The larger the number of persons working in hospitals (1.1.1)
The greater the resources invested in hospitals (1.2 and 1.3)
The greater the utilization of hospitals (1.4 and 1.5)
The earlier are referrals (1.6) and consequently the higher the rate of recovery (6.1)

The more extensive are religions teaching that illness can be reversed by practical human action (A.3), then:

The larger the number of persons working in hospitals (1.1.1)
The greater the resources invested in hospitals (1.2 and 1.3)
The more advanced the skills of hospital workers (1.1.2)
The greater the utilization of hospitals (1.4 and 1.5)
The earlier are referrals (1.6) and consequently the higher the rate of recovery (6.1)
The greater the stress on the hospital's therapeutic goals (4.1)
The higher the rate of clinical innovation (4.6)

The more extensive a denomination's ecclesiastic organization (A.4), then:

The greater the utilization of hospitals because of demand by clerics and members of the denomination (1.4 and 1.5)
The larger the number of hospitals in national networks (5.2)
The wider the standardization in the organization and performance of hospitals (5.3)
The greater the recruitment of hospital employees (1.1.1)
The more evenly distributed are the skilled workers and resources of hospitals (1.7, 2.3.1, 2.3.2)
The later the entry of professionally trained personnel into hospitals (1.1.2)
The greater the control over the hospital from outside (3.1)
The weaker the authority of lay professionals and administrators (3.2)
The lower the consensus over goals and organizational procedure, after skilled laymen are introduced (3.3, 3.4, and 4.5)

The greater the number of religions in a society (A.5), then:

The more diffused the ownership and management of hospitals (5.2)

The smaller the average hospital (2.1)

The stronger the clerical influence over goals and management (3.1, 3.2, 4.2)

Within each hospital, the greater the consensus over goals and management (3.4 and 4.5)

Throughout the society, the lower the consensus over goals and management (3.4 and 4.5)

Within publicly owned hospitals, the lower the consensus over goals and management (3.4 and 4.5)

The longer are working hours (4.9)

The greater the functional specificity between religion and medicine (A.6), then:

The greater the utilization of the hospital (1.4 and 1.5)

The greater the number of skilled lay clinicians in hospitals (1.1.1 and 1.1.2)

The weaker the spiritual motives for employment (1.1.4)

The greater the authority of lay clinicians (3.2)

The lower the tensions between clinicians and clerics over goals and management (3.3, 3.4, 4.5)

The more consistent the provision of services according to patients' medical needs rather than personal characteristics (4.3)

The higher the rate of clinical innovation (4.6)

The shorter are working hours (4.9)

The fewer the conflicting demands by the employee's nonmedical social statuses (4.8)

The fewer the disputes over goals and the rate of success (6.4)

Notes

1. Jurgen Ruesch, "The Healing Traditions: Some Assumptions Made by Physicians," in Iago Galdston (ed.), *Man's Image in Medicine and Anthropology* (New York: International Universities Press, 1963), pp. 506–507. Various theories of disease in primitive and modern societies are summarized throughout Galdston's book.

2. How theories of disease relate to both the antecedent culture and to the derived methods of prevention and treatment is described in Paul Fejos, "Magic, Witchcraft

and Medical Theory in Primitive Cultures," *ibid.*, pp. 52–55; Charles C. Hughes, "Medical Care: Ethnomedicine," *International Encyclopedia of the Social Sciences* (New York: Macmillan & The Free Press, 1968), 10: 87–92; and Margaret Read, *Culture, Health, and Disease* (London: Tavistock Publications, 1966), Ch. 4.

3. II *Kings*, XV:5, and II *Chron.*, XXVI:21.

4. *Deut.*, X:19. Also *Lev.*, XIX:17–18.

5. *Passim*, esp. *Deut.*, XV:7–11 and *Lev.*, XXV:35.

6. *Ex.*, XXII:20–25, and numerous other passages cited by Ellsworth Faris et al., *Intelligent Philanthropy* (Chicago: The University of Chicago Press, 1930), pp. 55–76; and by Ephraim Frisch, *An Historical Survey of Jewish Philanthropy* (New York: Macmillan, 1924), pp. 6–30.

7. Frisch, *Jewish Philanthropy,* pp. 34–40 and 100–124.

8. Immanuel Jakobovits, *Jewish Medical Ethics* (New York: Philosophical Library, 1959), pp. 106–108.

9. *Ibid.*, pp. 1–7.

10. Yehezkel Kaufman, *The Religion of Israel* (Chicago: The University of Chicago Press, 1960), pp. 106–108.

11. E.g., *Num.*, XII:10–15 and XXI:6–9; II *Kings*, V:1–27; and *Isa.*, XXXVIII:21.

12. Jakobovits, *Jewish Medical Ethics*, pp. 24–41. One exception is the deviant *Hassidim* of Eastern Europe. They believed their leaders, the *tsaddikim*, had prophetic powers, and they relied on the *tsaddikim* for miraculous cures. Mark Zborowski and Elizabeth Herzog, *Life Is With People—The Jewish Little-Town of Eastern Europe* (New York: International Universities Press, 1952), pp. 172-173 and 355.

13. Salo W. Baron, *The Jewish Community* (Philadelphia: The Jewish Publication Society of America, 1942), Vol. I, pp. 362–363; Vol. II, pp. 327–329; and Vol. III, pp. 90–93.

14. *Ibid.*, Vol. II, pp. 327–329; and Vol. III, pp. 210, 212.

15. Because of dietary laws, a Jewish patient could be treated only at home or in a hospital run by his community. Only in the late nineteenth century in the United States did there develop a Jewish community whose members would live in places serving nonkosher food.

16. *Matt.*, passim, especially Ch. IX.

17. *Matt.*, X:8 and XXV:36–46; *Luke*, X:27.

18. E.g., *Rom.*, XVI:1–2.

19. *Mark*, VII:24–30.

20. *Mark*, II:5, and *John*, IX:2. If the sin was deemed serious and unforgivable, and if disease was considered an appropriate divine punishment, this reasoning would imply that secular medical care is futile and undesirable, and that patients should be avoided. After the early centuries, Christianity increasingly distinguished between soul and body and between sin and sickness. Rather, it was increasingly believed, illnesses are largely due to the weaknesses of the earthly body, from which Christ too suffered. As a result, Christianity encourages greater respect and sympathy for patients than do most other religions, according to Henry E. Sigerist, *On the History of Medicine* (New York: MD Publications, 1960), pp. 8 and 27.

21. *Epistle of James*, V:14–18.

22. Christian and Jewish scholars now dispute whether these rooms or their Hebrew counterparts were the first true hospitals, e.g., compare Gerhard Uhlhorn, *Christian Charity in the Ancient Church* (New York: Charles Scribner's Sons, 1883), pp. 323–338; and Joseph Jacobs, "Hospital," *The Jewish Encyclopedia* (New York: Funk and Wagnalls, 1904), Vol. 6, pp. 479–480.

23. In contrast, the Jews in the Diaspora were a pariah people who never assimilated the attitudes and skills of modern bureaucracy and of industrial labor. Max Weber, *The Sociology of Religion* (Boston: Beacon Press, 1963), p. 250. Therefore the Christians but not the Jews could develop large-scale formal organization for the performance of good works.

24. For the history of European hospitals and their relationship to Christian Churches, see George Rosen, "The Hospital—Historical Sociology of a Community Institution," in Eliot Freidson (ed.), *The Hospital in Modern Society* (New York: The Free Press, 1963), Ch. 1; and Edward D. Churchill, "The Development of the Hospital," in Nathaniel W. Faxon (ed.), *The Hospital in Contemporary Life* (Cambridge: Harvard University Press, 1949), pp. 1–69.

25. Good comparisons of Catholic and Protestant doctrines and of their consequences for social services appear in Faris et al., *Intelligent Philanthropy*, pp. 112–120.

26. Ernst Benz, *The Eastern Orthodox Church—Its Thought and Life* (Garden City, N.Y.: Doubleday, 1963), passim, especially pp. 90, 100, 152, 162, and 214. A few Russian *laymen* organized groups of nurses during the nineteenth century, somewhat like the German *Mutterhäuser*. Religious appeals were used to recruit members, and religious ceremonies were part of their daily routine. But the initiative, management, and work of these small orders were lay. E. D. Ashurkov et al., "The Work and Training of Feldshers and Nurses in the USSR," *Aspects of Public Health Nursing* (Geneva: World Health Organization, 1961), p. 159. Anton Chekhov's novel, *Ward 6*, describes the decrepitude of hospitals in a country where neither Church nor State felt responsible. Such a complete vacuum did not exist in the West.

27. For example, nursing was introduced into predominantly Orthodox Rumania

by Catholic and Lutheran missionaries, because the Orthodox nuns were preoccupied with praying, fasting, spinning, and caring for orphans. Elise Bucsan, "The Influence of Latin Ideals and Traditions on Nursing Education in Roumania," in *International Aspects of Nursing Education* (New York: Bureau of Publications, Teachers' College, 1932), pp. 31–32.

28. On *zakat*, see the *Koran*, II:43 and LVIII:13; Sayed Kotb, *Social Justice in Islam* (Washington: American Council of Learned Societies, 1953), pp. 73–74 and 133–137; and Reuben Levy, *The Social Structure of Islam* (Cambridge: The University Press, 1957), pp. 159–160. On *sadaquat*, see the *Koran*, IV:114 and IX:60; and Kotb, *Social Justice in Islam*, pp. 74–81. Atonement for sins and rewards is described in the *Koran*, II:270–273, IV:114, IX:103, and LVII:18. Punishment for failure to give alms is described in the *Koran*, IX:79, LXIX:30–37, LXXXIX:17–30, and CVII:1–7.

29. Sami Hamarneh, "Development of Hospitals in Islam," *Journal of the History of Medicine and Allied Sciences*, 17:3 (July 1962), 366–384.

30. Naguib Mahfouz, *The History of Medical Education in Egypt* (Cairo: Government Press, Bulaq, 1935), pp. 12–15.

31. James Robson, "Magic Cures in Popular Islam," *The Moslem World*, 24 (January 1934), 33–44; Samuel Zwemer, *The Influence of Animism on Islam* (London: Central Board of Missions, 1920), Ch. 9; Ailon Shiloh, "The System of Medicine in the Middle East Culture," *The Middle East Journal*, 15:3 (Summer 1961), 277–288; J. Spencer Trimingham, *Islam in the Sudan* (London: Oxford University Press, 1949), pp. 163–178; and A. F. A. Husain, *Human and Social Impact of Technological Change in Pakistan* (Dacca: Oxford University Press, 1956), Vol. I, pp. 66–67.

32. Raphael Patai, "Religion in Middle Eastern, Far Eastern, and Western Culture," *Southwestern Journal of Anthropology*, 10:3 (Autumn 1954), 240–241.

33. Reuben Levy, *The Social Structure of Islam* (Cambridge: The University Press, 1957), Ch. 5 passim; and Arthur Jeffery, *Islam: Muhammad and His Religion* (New York: The Liberal Arts Press, 1958), pp. 147–154.

34. E.g., Afif I. Tannous, "Extension Work Among the Arab Fellahin," in Edmund Brunner et al. (eds.), *Farmers of the World* (New York: Columbia University Press, 1945), pp. 89 and 94–95.

35. E.g., Kenneth W. Morgan, *The Path of the Buddha* (New York: Ronald Press, 1956), p. 244.

36. E.g., *Public Health in Thailand* (Bangkok: Ministry of Public Health, 1960), pp. 17–18.

37. E.g., L. M. Hanks and Jane R. Hanks, "Diphtheria Immunization in a Thai Community," in Benjamin D. Paul (ed.), *Health, Culture, and Community: Case Studies of Public Reactions to Health Programs* (New York: Russell Sage Foundation, 1955), p. 171.

38. Bouquet believes that some doctrines about salvation through ascetic individual spiritual self-management have always militated against social service. A. C. Bouquet, *Comparative Religion* (Harmondsworth: Penguin Books, 3rd ed., 1950), p. 130.

39. Avinash Chandra Kaviratna, *Charaka-Samhita* (Calcutta: D. C. Dass, 1890), pp. 168–171.

40. D. B. Jelliffe and F. J. Bennett, "Indigenous Medical Systems and Child Health," *The Journal of Pediatrics*, 57:2 (August 1960), 251.

41. Max Weber, *The Religion of India* (New York: The Free Press, 1958), pp. 235–243.

42. Henry R. Zimmer, *Hindu Medicine* (Baltimore: The Johns Hopkins Press, 1948), pp. 86–88.

43. Max Weber, *From Max Weber: Essays in Sociology* (New York: Oxford University Press, 1946), pp. 271–272. On the reliance of diagnostic and therapeutic methods upon the religions in preindustrial societies, see David Bidney, "So-Called Primitive Medicine and Religion," in Galdston, *Man's Image*, pp. 141–156; and T. Adeoye Lambo, *African Traditional Beliefs, Concepts of Health, and Medical Practice* (Ibadan: Ibadan University Press, 1963).

44. Max Weber, *The Sociology of Religion* (Boston: Beacon Press, 1963), p. xxxi and Ch. 3.

45. Erwin H. Ackerknecht, "Problems of Primitive Medicine," *The Bulletin of the History of Medicine*, 11:5 (May 1942), 503–521; Erwin H. Ackerknecht, "Primitive Medicine and Culture Pattern," *ibid.*, 12:4 (November 1942), 545–572; Henry E. Sigerist, *A History of Medicine: Primitive and Archaic Medicine* (New York: Oxford University Press, 1951), Ch. 2; and Lewis S. S. O'Malley, *Popular Hinduism* (Cambridge: The University Press, 1935), pp. 142–153 and 160. Preindustrial and developing societies have three medical roles that may be combined by the same folk doctor: the diviner of the causes of the disease or injury; the specialist in combatting supernatural causes of the affliction; the purveyor of physical or herbal treatments to restore the patient's body. George Way Harley, *Native African Medicine* (Cambridge: Harvard University Press, 1941), p. 200. The methods of African folk doctors are described in Michael Gelfand, *Medicine and Custom in Africa* (Edinburgh: E. & S. Livingstone, 1964), Chs. 3, 4, and 5; and Margaret Read, *Culture, Health, and Disease*, Ch. 3. The resemblance to the folk doctors of Islam is evident from Shiloh, "System of Medicine," pp. 285–288.

46. M. G. Marwick, "Social Structure," in *African Culture and Its Relation to the Training of African Nurses* (Johannesburg: Transvaal Nursing Education Discussion Group, South African Nursing Association, 1954).

47. Erwin H. Ackerknecht, "Natural Diseases and Rational Treatment in Primitive Medicine," *The Bulletin of the History of Medicine*, 29:5 (May 1946), 467–497; Sigerist, *History of Medicine*, pp. 201–209; Milton I. Roemer, *Medical Care in*

Latin America (Washington: Pan American Union, 1963), p. 12; Harley, *Native African Medicine*, Ch. 6 and Supplement; and Shiloh, "System of Medicine," pp. 279–280 and 286–288. The gradual decline in folk medicine in Northern India— so that ultimately it is sought only for chronic incapacitating illness—is described by Harold A. Gould, "The Implications of Technical Change for Folk and Scientific Medicine," *American Anthropologist*, 59:3 (June 1957), 507–516.

48. E. C. Jali, "Magic and Witchcraft in the Hospital Ward, in *African Culture and Its Relation to the Training of African Nurses* ; Ozzie G. Simmons, "Popular and Modern Medicine in Mestizo Communities of Coastal Peru and Chile," in Dorrian Apple (ed.), *Sociological Studies of Health and Sickness* (New York: McGraw-Hill, 1960), pp. 80–84; Paul, *Health, Culture, and Community*, pp. 30–32 and 126–129; and Hamed Ammar, "The Sociological Approach to Problems of Community Development" (Sirs-el-Layyan, Egypt: unpublished paper of the Arab States Fundamental Education Centre, 1960).

49. Such experiences harmed the Catholic Church's standing in Italy during the nineteenth century. Although the Church resisted the nationalization bills in the late 1880s, ultimately it benefitted from being relieved of responsibility. Nationalization is described by Henry C. Burdett, *Hospitals and Asylums of the World* (London: J. & A. Churchill, 1893), Vol. III, pp. 554–556.

50. Large proportions of the general hospitals are owned by religious associations in Holland, Germany, Switzerland, and the United States, according to the statistics in "Overzicht van de Gegevens der Ziekenhuizen in Nederland over de Jaren 1958 en 1959," *Verslagen en Mededelingen Betreffende de Volksgezondheid*, 9 (September 1961), 496–497 and 699–702; T. E. Chester and Gordon Forsyth, "Health and Hospital Services in the Netherlands," *The Hospital*, 56:2 (February 1960), 109– 110; *Report of Study Tour of Hospitals in the German Federal Republic* (London: International Hospital Federation, 1958), pp. 38–39; Hans Aregger, "Das Kranken- hauswesen in der Schweiz," *Plan: Schweizerische Zeitschrift für Landes- Regional- und Ortsplanung*, 12:5 (May 1955), 108; and "Hospital Statistics, 1961," *The Hospital*, 36:15, Part 2 (1 August 1962), 420. Arguments on behalf of denomina- tional ownership of hospitals in Holland appear in Jos Maenen, *Het Ziekenhuis in Het Totaal van de Gezondheidszorg* ('s-Gravenhage: Vereniging van Katholieke Ziekenhuizen, 1958).

51. "Overzicht van de Gegevens der Ziekenhuizen in Nederland over de Jaren 1958 en 1959," pp. 491–495.

52. On competition among doctors in Beirut, see François Dupré La Tour, "Médecins et malades au Liban," *Travaux et jours*, 34:3 (October–December 1961), 21–39.

53. Adelaide M. Nutting and Lavinia L. Dock, *A History of Nursing* (New York: Putnam, 1907–1912), Vols. I and II.

54. E.g., Joseph H. Fichter, *Religion as an Occupation* (South Bend, Ind.: Univer- sity of Notre Dame Press, 1961), pp. 128–131. One of the surviving medieval

nursing brotherhoods is the Order of the Fatebene-Fratelli, which still runs its hospital on the historic island in the Tiber River where medical facilities have stood continuously since the Roman Empire. Nutting and Dock, *History of Nursing*, Vol. I, pp. 85 and 337–338.

55. For simplicity, I shall use the word "order" to refer to both nuns and Deaconesses. The latter are an association of religious with the same Mother House. In our conversations, Deaconesses often preferred to avoid the word "order" since they wished to distinguish themselves from nuns, whom they believe are more organized and disciplined.

56. E.g., Fritz Hoch, *Hundert Jahre Diakonissenanstalt Riehen* (Basel: Verlag Friedrich Reinhardt A.G., 1952), pp. 99–105.

57. On the contraction and aging of the religious nursing orders in Switzerland, see Rosmarie Lang and Magdelaine Comtesse, *Les services infirmiers en Suisse face aux exigences actuelles et futures* (Berne: La Croix-Rouge Suisse, 1959), pp. 46–54 passim; Hoch, *Hundert Jahre*, p. 162; and *Jahresbericht* (Riehen: Diakonissenhaus, 1958), p. 10.

58. Lang and Comtesse, *Les services infirmiers en Suisse*, p. 39.

59. Nutting and Dock, *History of Nursing*, Vol. II, Chs. 5–7 passim; and Cecil Woodham-Smith, *Florence Nightingale, 1820–1910* (New York: McGraw-Hill, 1951), passim.

60. Everett C. Hughes, *Twenty Thousand Nurses Tell Their Story* (Philadelphia: Lippincott, 1958), p. 37; Robert M. Frumkin, *The Nurse as a Human Being* (Buffalo: University Bookstore, University of Buffalo, 1956), pp. 6–7; Ann C. Hansen, "Can More Nurses Be Recruited?" *New York State Nurse*, 30:4 (May 1958), 9; M. Mury, "Sociologie des élèves infirmières: Compte-rendu de l'enquête" (Sevres: unpublished paper presented to the Journées d'étude reservées aux monitrices des écoles, 1961), p. 11.

61. Rose K. Goldsen and Rodney F. White, "A Study of Professional Attitudes Towards Work: The Case of Nursing" (New York: unpublished paper presented to the American Sociological Association meetings, 1960), p. 9.

62. Ray E. Trussell et al., *Medical and Hospital Care in Puerto Rico* (New York: School of Public Health and Administrative Medicine, Columbia University, 1962), pp. 156, 170.

63. Published sources of the data cited in the text: Johannesburg, from E. W. Petersen, "African Nurse Training—Ten Years of Progress," *Medical Proceedings* 4:10 (17 May 1958), 329. Lebanon 1905–1955, from Ruth F. Woodsmall and Charlotte Johnson, *Study of the Role of Women: Their Activities and Organizations in Lebanon, Egypt, Iraq, Jordan and Syria* (New York: The International Federation of Business and Professional Women, 1956), p. 13. Iraq, from Woodsmall and Johnson, *Role of Women*, p. 44. Indonesia, from Ruth Woodsmall, *Women and the New East* (Washington: The Middle East Institute, 1960), pp. 208–209 and 217.

Pakistan and India, from Pauline Estelle King, "Potential Use of Nurses in Primary Health Centers in Madras State, India" (New York: unpublished dissertation for the Ed.D. in Nursing Education, Columbia University, 1962), Ch. 3, p. 6 and Ch. 5, p. 19; and Alice Wilkinson, *A Brief History of Nursing in India and Pakistan* (Delhi: The Trained Nurses' Association of India, 1958), p. 31.

64. A. H. Hourani, *Minorities in the Arab World* (London: Oxford University Press, 1947), pp. 67–68.

65. John E. Owen, "Nursing in Pakistan," *Nursing Times,* 57:12 (24 March 1961), 377.

66. King, "Potential Use of Nurses," Ch.3, p. 6, and Ch. 5, p. 19.

67. E.g., B. Seebohm Rowntree and G. R. Lavers, *English Life and Leisure—A Social Study* (London: Longmans, Green, 1951), pp. 342–343, 351–353 and 366–368; and Michael Argyle, *Religious Behavior* (New York: The Free Press, 1959), pp. 23–28.

68. Richard H. Shryock, *The History of Nursing* (Philadelphia: Saunders, 1959), Chs. 5–8; Paul Diepgen, *Die Theologie und der ärztliche Stand im Mittelalter* (Berlin: W. Rothschild, 1922); Paul Diepgen, *Über den Einfluss der autoritativen Theologie auf die Medizin des Mittelalters* (Mainz: Verlag der Akademie der Wissenschaften und der Literatur, 1958); and David Riesman, *The Story of Medicine in the Middle Ages* (New York: Hoeber, 1935).

69. Woodsmall and Johnson, *Role of Women*, p. 12.

70. Edward Wakin, "The Copts in Egypt," *Middle Eastern Affairs,* 12:7 (August–September 1961), 200–201.

71. E.g., Ivan Belknap, *Human Problems of a State Mental Hospital* (New York: McGraw-Hill, 1956), p. 251.

72. Alick Cameron, "Folklore as a Medical Problem Among Arab Refugees," *The Practitioner,* 185:1107 (September 1960), 347–349; and Afif I. Tannous, "Extension Work Among the Arab Fellahin," in Edmund Brunner et al. (eds.), *Farmers of the World* (New York: Columbia University Press, 1945), p. 89.

73. King, "Potential Use of Nurses," Ch. 6, p. 14.

74. Thomas S. McPartland, *Formal Education and the Process of Professionalization: A Study of Student Nurses* (Kansas City, Mo.: Community Studies, 1957), pp. 16–17, 50–51, 56–58, 64–65, and 85. On the correlations between the attitudinal implications of individualistic religions such as Protestantism and propensity to enter work emphasizing achievement amidst uncertainty—such as business and medicine—see David C. McClelland, *The Achieving Society* (Princeton: Van Nostrand, 1961), pp. 356–372. If, as McClelland's data suggest, the need for achievement is highly associated with Protestantism while the need for affiliation is highly associated with Catholicism, then it is not surprising that medicine gains many recruits among Protestants while nursing is particularly attractive to Catholics.

75. Irwin Deutscher, *A Survey of the Social and Occupational Characteristics of a Metropolitan Nursing Complement* (Kansas City, Mo.: Community Studies, November 1956), pp. 126–128; and Irwin Deutscher and Ann Montague, "Professional Education and Conflicting Value Systems," *Social Forces*, 35:2 (December 1956), 126–131.

76. Daily schedules for all the French nursing orders appear in the appendices of some of the volumes in the series entitled *Les grands ordres réligieux* (Paris: Librairie Letouzey et Ané, 1923–1931, 55 vols.).

77. Charles-Louis Gagnebin, *Rapport annuel* (Saint-Loup: Institution des Diaconesses, 1960), pp. 2–3. Other eloquent statements of the meaning of apostolic work for Protestant Deaconesses and Catholic nuns appear in Rodolphe von Tavel, *La puissance et la gloire* (Berne: Maison des Diaconesses, 1935), pp. 80–89; and Léon Joseph Cardinal Suenens, *The Nun in the World* (Westminster, Md.: The Newman Press, 2nd ed., 1963).

78. Joseph H. Fichter, *Religion as an Occupation* (South Bend, Ind.: University of Notre Dame Press, 1961), pp. 148–151.

79. E.g., Nutting and Dock, *History of Nursing*, Vol. I, p. 318; Vol. II, pp. 245–246; and Vol. III, pp. 289–290.

80. F. Campbell Stewart, *The Hospitals and Surgeons of Paris* (New York: Langley, 1843), p. 55.

81. But, emphasize these Superiors, the religious must not become so professionalized in nursing and so dedicated to hospital routine that she neglects spiritual care to patients. Suenens, *The Nun in the World*, pp. 88–90.

82. The theory and methods of reconciling modern hospital practice and the religious order's traditional views and procedures are summarized in *ibid.*, Ch. 10.

83. *Rapport annuel* (Saint-Loup: Institution des Diaconesses, 1959), p. 13.

84. Pius XII, "On Religious Vocations," *The Catholic Mind*, 51:1086 (June 1953), 381; and Suenens, *The Nun in the World*, pp. 147–153.

85. Normally an organization is uniform and free of ambiguities in the status and compliance structures of its elites. Thus Etzioni's organizational types are internally consistent and stable. Amitai Etzioni, *A Comparative Analysis of Complex Organizations* (New York: The Free Press, 1961), Ch. 9. But when a religious order works in a modern hospital, the organization becomes a mixture of two of his types, with consequent strain: a religious order consists of a hierarchy of charismatics and a secular hospital is an organization ruled by a top layer of charismatics (i.e., the doctors), but there are no clear principles governing compliance between two very different sorts of charismatics.

86. No problems confront the Protestant Deaconesses, who have almost completely disappeared from public hospitals. Strains experienced by the Deaconess working by herself in a public hospital are one of the reasons Deaconesses have been withdrawn. For example, a leader of a Deaconess association explained some of the

reasons why members no longer work in a nearby teaching hospital: "The other lay nurses in the university hospital mock the Deaconesses. Also, the young Deaconesses can see the other lay nurses go home after so many hours a day, after 7 P.M. It is a constant temptation for a young girl to be there."

87. Menial work is conspicuous during the nursing education of many nuns. Some orders emphasize its penitential significance for a religious, and thus it is an important symbol to retain: e.g., Kathryn Hulme, *The Nun's Story* (Boston: Little, Brown, 1956), pp. 14–15.

88. The meaning and application of the concepts of "sacred" and "profane" in many religions are elaborated in the writings of Mircea Eliade, particularly *The Sacred and the Profane* (New York: Harcourt, Brace, 1959); and *Traité d'histoire des réligions* (Paris: Payot, 2nd ed., 1964).

89. The Christian and Jewish literature—including the theological controversies —is reviewed thoroughly by Jakobovits, *Jewish Medical Ethics*, Ch. 14. No religion officially condemns abortions and birth control on the grounds that people are obligated to have the maximum number of children, although some clergymen recruited from the mass public may vulgarize official doctrine in this way; e.g., Ivan Gadourek, *A Dutch Community* (Leiden: H. E. Stenfert Kroese N.V., 1956), pp. 94 and 177; Frank Lorimer, *Culture and Human Fertility* (Paris: U.N.E.S.C.O., 1954), p. 187; and Hamed Ammar, *Growing Up in an Egyptian Village* (London: Routledge & Kegan Paul, 1954), p. 97. Many Catholic critics of abortions and birth control have commended large families as signs of God's blessing, and some have come close to urging the largest possible families. George A. Kelley, *Overpopulation: A Catholic View* (New York: Paulist Press, 1960), pp. 56–57.

90. *Survey of Legislation on Marriage, Divorce and Related Topics Relevant to Population* (New York: Bureau of Social Affairs, Population Branch, The United Nations, 1956); Clyde V. Kiser, *Research in Family Planning* (Princeton: Princeton University Press, 1962), passim, especially pp. 235–242; and Theodor von Miltner, "Die Gesetzgebung der Kulturvölker zum Problem der Fruchtabtreibung," *Archiv für Gynaekologie*, 142:1 (July 1930), 133–151. It is difficult to add to the following paragraphs about how religion makes a difference among countries in hospital abortion rates, in part because of the unreliability of statistics for cross-national comparisons. For estimates of total incidence, see *Foetal, Infant, and Early Childhood Mortality* (New York: Bureau of Social Affairs, Population Branch, The United Nations, 1954), pp. 16–23; Kiser, *Research in Family Planning*, pp. 235–242; and *Proceedings of the Eighth International Conference of the International Planned Parenthood Federation*, 1967, pp. 129–153.

91. Cicely Watson, "Birth Control and Abortion in France Since 1939," *Population Studies*, 5:3 (March 1952), 266–268. Certain racial philosophies may motivate antiabortion policies, even if simultaneous Church influence were absent. For example, pre-Nazi Germany banned abortions in public hospitals because of the influence of its two principal Churches, Catholicism and Evangelical Christianity. Nazism, which might be considered a conservative folk religion, also opposed abortions and tightened the administration of earlier policies.

92. Mary Steichen Calderone, *Abortion in the United States* (New York: Hoeber-Harper, 1958), pp. 200–206.

93. Sigerist, *History of Medicine*, pp. 36–37.

94. Compare Ahmed Kamel Mazen, "Development of the Medical Program of the Egyptian Region of the United Arab Republic" (Stanford: unpublished dissertation for the Ph.D. in Medical Care Administration, Stanford University, 1961), p. 220; with "Hospital Statistics, 1961," *Hospitals,* 36:15, Part 2 (August 1962), 414.

95. E. A. Beet, "The Daily Life of a Doctor in Kano, Nigeria," *Central African Journal of Medicine*, 3:10 (October 1957), 414.

96. E.g., Robert C. Stever, "Medical Impressions from India and Nepal," *The Journal of Medical Education*, 36:4 (April 1961), 332–335.

97. Jakobovits, *Jewish Medical Ethics*, Ch. 15.

98. E. A. Barker, "Rural Problems of Pediatrics," in *African Culture and Its Relation to the Training of African Nurses*.

99. Comparisons between death-denying and death-accepting religions in other areas are made by Franz Borkenau, "The Concept of Death," in Robert Fulton (ed.), *Death and Identity* (New York: Wiley, 1965), pp. 42–56. The changing attitudes toward death as society modernizes are described in the American case in Robert Fulton and Gilbert Geis, "Death and Social Values," in Fulton, *Death and Identity*, pp. 67–75.

100. I *Cor.*, XV:35–58.

101. Mary N. Alston, "The Attitude of the Church to Dissection Before 1500," *The Bulletin of the History of Medicine*, 16:3 (October 1944), 221–238; and Jack Kevorkian, *The Story of Dissection* (New York: Philosophical Library, 1959), pp. 34–44.

102. Many folk religions say that a person cannot join his ancestors unless his body is complete at burial. So African tribesmen, for example, often resist surgery. Amputations may be accepted only if the removed limb accompanies the patient back to his village for future burial. P. Keen, "Surgical Problems in Bantu Practice," in *African Culture and Its Relation to the Training of African Nurses*.

103. Maurice Gaudefroy-Demombynes, *Muslim Institutions* (London: Allen & Unwin, 1950), pp. 171–173.

104. J. W. H. Stobart, *Islam and Its Founder* (London: Society for Promoting Christian Knowledge, 1901), pp. 205–207.

105. Hamarneh, "Development of Hospitals in Islam," p. 383.

106. Mahfouz, *Medical Education in Egypt*, p. 31. (*Ulemas* are Muslim scholars or men of authority in religion and law.)

107. E.g., Beet, "The Daily Life of a Doctor in Kano, Nigeria," p. 411. These

religious objections forced abandonment of a blood transfusion service and corneal transplants in Beet's northern Nigerian hospital. Similar Orthodox Jewish opposition to dissection in Israel has been directed against corneal transplants as well as against post-mortems.

108. *Gen.*, I:26–27.

109. Jakobovits, *Jewish Medical Ethics*, Ch. 12; and Zborowski and Herzog, *Life Is With People*, p. 357.

110. Jakobovits, *Jewish Medical Ethics*, pp. 149–152.

111. An example of the protest literature is *Compulsory Post-Mortem Operations in Israel* (Jerusalem: Committee for Safeguarding Human Dignity, 1967).

112. E.g., Jakobovits, *Jewish Medical Ethics*, pp. 45–51, 57, and 84; and Levy, *Social Structure of Islam*, pp. 160–161.

113. Numerous food avoidances are described by Frederick J. Simoons, *Eat Not This Flesh: Food Avoidances in the Old World* (Madison: The University of Wisconsin Press, 1961).

114. Jakobovits, *Jewish Medical Ethics*, pp. 74–81.

3

The Family

One of the several tasks of the family in most societies is the protection and solace of individuals during physical and emotional trouble. Social norms designate family members as bearing the principal obligation to the person in trouble; affection and respect motivate them to act accordingly. Hospitals are unusual among formal organizations in that clients have more than fleeting contact, become integrated into the structure, and must play definite roles. Therefore fundamental differences among societies are whether the family system enables members to join the hospital for treatment and whether the family requires any adaptations in the patient roles that the hospitals customarily define according to clinical procedures.

Another important intersection between family and hospital is whether women are allowed to work there. Nearly every form of hospital relies heavily on the labor of women. Therefore, among the crucial determinants of the extent and performance of hospital services are the freedom of women to work in the market economy generally, the freedom of women to perform the type of work required in hospitals, the amount of education given the available classes of women, and the skills and behavior expected of women in such jobs.

Demand for Hospitalization

All societies, whether primitive or modern, have some kind of medical care dispensed by specialists. But most societies expect the patient to be kept at home and served by his family.[1] In agrarian tribal societies, folk doctors treat the patient on an ambulatory basis in their own homes or at special ceremonial places; or they make house calls to bedridden patients. Only rarely does any establishment resembling a hospital appear in a primitive society, and it assists rather than replaces care by the family. A few buildings may spring up near a famous folk doctor's work site, to accommodate patients and family members travelling from afar and to store the medications. Some folk doctors have invented regimens of long silence, long rest, supervised diet, and custodial protection from evil influences, and therefore they have built accommodations for patients and family members.[2]

For many centuries in the West, Islamic nations, and India, patient care likewise was assumed to be the function of the family. Hospitals were primarily for persons without families nearby, such as members of religious orders, soldiers, travelers, and the homeless poor.

Modern Western hospitals spread to countries undergoing modernization. In addition some of these countries have a second type of hospital, somewhat like a large outpatient clinic with beds. Like the establishments created by folk practitioners, it incorporates into the organization not only the patient but also his family, since the family does the nursing. This type of hospital has one or a few central buildings, with an operating room, first-aid and bandaging rooms, a laboratory, a pharmacy, offices and some beds for critical and postoperative cases. The staff consists of one or a few doctors, a few professional and practical nurses, and some auxiliaries and porters. If the hospital is located near population centers, most of the care is ambulatory. If the hospital's clientele comes from large distances, a village of smaller buildings may spring up around the central buildings, in order to house patients and their families overnight or for a few days. The families provide the nursing and cooking in the outbuildings, some of which they erected themselves. In countries with lingering tribal enmities, such as several regions of Africa, different parts of the hospital grounds may be set aside for different tribes.[3] Some of these hospitals evolved without plan from rural health centers that were unexpectedly overwhelmed and altered by large numbers of ambulatory patients. Others were deliberately designed to reproduce tribal living conditions, so that patients and their families would not resist hospitalization.[4]

Family institutions are among the last to change when a social system modernizes, and therefore the inpatient's dependence on the family may continue long after other aspects of the hospital have adopted the most modern forms of organization under the authority of doctors and nurses. A graduate nurse is in charge of the ward, but ward society consists of both patients and their families. Some family members live on the hospital grounds, while others live in town and have virtually unlimited visiting privileges.[5] In parts of Africa, Asia, Japan and Balkan rural areas, the hospitals have virtually come to incorporate family members into the organization in order to provide the patient with his customary diet, personal services, and emotional support. This proves more economical for the hospital; nurses might be reluctant to give personal services (such as baths or handling of excretions) to patients; and perhaps male patients might refuse to accept personal services from any but kinsmen. The patient may learn the roles expected by the hospital, but controlling the family is more difficult: family members sometimes spread folk remedies and native diets through the ward to supplement the hospital's therapies, and the spoons and soap may disappear.[6] European-trained graduate nurses are often distressed at the disorder and picnicking by exuberant healthy family members in a setting defined by their training as a place exclusively for quiet and easily controlled patients.[7]

Some hospitals take advantage of the educational opportunities arising from the family's presence. They give health training to family members, and thereby the hospital becomes a modernizing force.[8]

Most highly modern countries restrict the family to the role of guests during fixed hours, and all nursing and catering are performed by the hospital's own staff. But in a few countries, kinship ties remain strong and cause an "uneven" development in hospital structures. For example, Japanese hospitals resemble those of other developed countries in equipment, medical staffing, and medical care, but the patient's family continues to do much of the nursing.[9]

The hospitalization of women. In all underdeveloped countries in the recent past and in their rural areas today, women of all social classes have been expected to remain within the family circle. Living in a passive manner among strangers violates widespread taboos against threats to female chastity. Adverse rumors about a woman dishonor her male relatives in Islamic and many other societies, are grounds for divorce, and damage her marriage prospects. Any contact with male doctors—much less prolonged submission to their control—may be avoided even at the risk of death.[10] The family cannot spare the woman for long periods, since she cares for children, cooks, and does other essential housework. Therefore, in Europe centuries ago and in underdeveloped countries lately, inpatient hospitalization consisted almost entirely of men plus a few women without families. At most, according to traditional customs in underdeveloped countries with strict sheltering of women, lower class women would visit outpatient clinics or receive Western female health visitors, while some upper class women receive private practitioners at home or temporarily drop out of the entire social system and seek hospital care abroad.

Increased willingness to become hospitalized is one of the trends in modernization of society. Positive social feedback is essential: a few women innovate by staying in wards, they return to their communities healthier and unsullied, their families profit from their recovery while other families continue to be burdened by chronically ill mothers and daughters, and other families then agree to send their women.[11] Hospitals ease the transition by staffing female wards with women and by allowing liberal visiting hours. As society modernizes, the family itself changes, making home care less feasible and reducing tolerance of chronically ill women. Extended family ties weaken, neolocal residence becomes more common, members of the family spend much of the day in organizations outside the home (such as the employer and school), and therefore fewer persons are available to care for sick people at home.[12] More women are employed by organizations whose rules of efficiency and regular attendance presuppose good health.

Therefore, as societies modernize, more women become hospital inpatients. Degrees of modernization result in different compositions of patient populations: women are a slight majority or only a slight minority of the general hospital inpatients (obstetrics and

gynecology excluded) in the developed countries, but men constitute three-fifths or more of the inpatients in less developed countries.[13]

If a country's religion emphasizes female modesty and chastity,
hospitals will be built and organized to separate patients by sex
rather than by medical function. For centuries European hospitals
consisted of at least two huge rooms separated by wide entrance
floors or gates; each room housed patients of the same sex but with
very different medical conditions. The visitor can still see the six-
teenth-century portions of the Ospedale di Santo Spirito in Rome
operated in this fashion: on either side of a wide entrance hall with
frescoes and an altar are two sixty-bed wards, one for male medical
patients and the other for female medical patients. Until the twentieth century, this was the entire hospital; now these two rooms still
contain over one-fifth of the hospital's patients. The decline of old
Catholic taboos about segregation of the sexes, the growing medical demands for technical convenience, and the construction of
small rooms have led to new arrangements of patients by medical
rather than sexual criteria. In most European countries, the newest
wards consist of patients with the same medical problem; within
each ward, separate rooms contain patients of different sex, but of
course now they are closer and meet more often than was possible
under the old system. Occasionally a further classification of patients is made by principles of progressive care, and the most
ambulatory men and women have many social contacts.

The Status of Women and
the Number of Nurses

The heart of the modern hospital is its nursing staff. Therefore the
position of women in the larger social system and in the family
determines the recruitment and performance of the hospital's personnel. Certain variables in the sex status are particularly important: whether women are allowed or expected to work outside the
home among strange men; whether women are allowed or expected
to do dirty work, domestic work, or personal service for strangers;
the extent of education for women; the extent and types of things

they know; and the extent of respect conferred upon the thoughts, actions, and authority of women. How these variables affect nursing depends on the woman's other personal and social characteristics, such as her age, marital status, maternal status, and social class. For example, as we shall see, whether the nurse is single or married will determine whether she is allowed to work outside the home and whether she is respected. Similarly, whether a woman is allowed to do certain menial tasks will depend on her social class origins.

Generalizations about the employment of nurses must take into account the cross-national variations in the position of women in the labor force. Such patterns are well known from previously published cross-national comparisons of census statistics. To summarize briefly, the less developed the country, the higher the percentage of its female labor force in agriculture and domestic service; the more developed the country, the higher the proportion in nondomestic services. At each level of development, Muslim countries have a lower rate of female participation in the public labor force and a higher proportion working at home. The more developed the country, the higher the percentage of women workers who are salaried employees and the lower the proportion who are unpaid family workers. In many developed countries, service occupations are overwhelmingly female.[14] These generalizations about the type of economy and the position of women in the labor force are only general background for the following analysis, since a number of more specific institutional conditions govern recruitment into nursing work, such as family structure, educational channels, the total opportunity structure for various classes of women, and the kind of nursing service expected by hospitals. Not all cross-national differences in family structure or the position of women are merely the results of religious or economic institutions.

Societies that shelter their women. Where women cannot become hospital inpatients, they cannot become hospital employees either. Women are expected to work on the farm, make handicrafts, prepare food, and care for children. Working with strangers is impossible, since coworkers are either kinswomen, kinsmen, or neighbors. Contact with male patients would be potential threats to chastity.

As a result of the barriers against female employment and female hospitalization, nursing was an entirely male occupation until recently in several countries. For example, in Yemen, Saudi Arabia, Kuwait, Bahrain, and some other conservative Muslim countries, the few hospitals until lately were created by governments just for male citizens or by oil companies primarily for their male employees. The male nurses usually would be trained in the hospital and sometimes would get additional training in Lebanese nursing schools.[15] Similarly, in much of Africa until recently the only hospital nurses with any formal training were men.[16]

Usually these countries have only a few hospitals and only a limited number of nursing jobs, and enough men apply. Since it is customary for men to nurse men, nursing does not have an image as a female occupation, as it does in the West. Male nurses are not the deviant members of a female occupation, their rise is not blocked by a system that reserves top jobs for women, they do not become subordinates of indigenous women, and they do not have the other problems of morale and career advancement that irritate male nurses in the West.[17] Since the patient's family gives the bedside care, the male nurse does no "dirty work" but performs the prestigious tasks of Western medicine, such as giving pills and injections.[18] In countries with much poverty and unemployment, nursing work may confer prestige rather than humiliation upon a man: he has a steady job and works in an organization that often exudes the glamour of advanced Western technique; many transfer from town hospitals to rural clinics, where they enjoy considerable local respect and do many responsible medical tasks with minimum supervision, such as sending patients to hospitals, prescribing and giving medicines, and doing minor surgery. Sometimes, particularly in Africa, these jobs have become the springboards for lucrative private practice, based on a combination of Western medicine, injection of black market antibiotics, and folk medicine.[19]

In the countries where, in the recent past, hospital inpatients and nurses were overwhelmingly male, a few women were admitted to the hospital, either because they were homeless town dwellers or had accidents. To take care of such patients, these Middle Eastern and African hospitals had small numbers of untrained female auxiliaries. Since they could not be salaried employees in the Western sense, with normal family relationships, they might have been foundlings, orphans, or homeless widows. High death rates in Middle Eastern cities and abandonment of girl babies always have produced some women who lived and worked in hospitals. (Centuries ago, some of the female employees of European hospitals were recruited in the same way.) Since women with normal family relationships remained in *purdah*, it was impossible to recruit groups in the modern fashion for training courses aimed at producing a better type of nurse or midwife. So, when a midwifery school was begun in Egypt during the 1830s, the first twenty women were bought on the slave market and the others were taken from orphan asylums.[20] For the next fifty years all recorded student midwives and student nurses in Egypt were slaves or orphans, and no upper class girl is known to have attended.[21]

Nursing by men and women. When women begin to become hospital inpatients, the staff must be recruited by sex. Male and female patients are kept in separate wards and often in separate buildings, with the nursing staff and attendants from the corresponding sex.[22] In some countries, such as India before independence, several hospitals may be established only for women and children, and even their medical staffs may be female.[23]

The increasing use of the hospital is part of an urban population movement that also transforms female life and female employment. In countries where the extended family is the basic unit of rural life, many lower class urban families are either conjugal or incomplete and disorganized. In the urban conjugal family the daughter and young wife are not continuously dominated by an older woman; if an older relative lives in the household, her status is guest rather than manager. The young women's friends are not exclusively relatives but include age peers from other families, so she discovers much about urban life and learns how to interact with strangers. The upper class urban family may be extended, as in rural areas, and the girl grows up under the domination of her elders; because family reputations and marriageability are more important than an extra wage, the upper class girl does not work outside the home.[24]

Many lower class daughters and young wives seek additional family income with the approval of fathers, husbands, or lovers. Young women of this class may soon become strongly committed to work, because for the first time it gives them spending money, recognition, and a stronger position within the family.[25] Lacking enough education for skilled work and barred by their sex from the majority of urban work, they often get unskilled odd jobs in domestic service and commerce; a few get less skilled factory jobs.[26] This female labor force usually lacks special training and has high turnover, but hospitals have many positions it can fill. Since the population generally contains few people with a good general education or specialized training, hospitals learn to get along with large numbers of unskilled persons in domestic work and nursing service, as is discussed in more detail in Chapter 4. Hospital work often is very attractive to women in these countries, because wages are better and employment can be steadier than for most alternatives.

Besides the desire for an extra wage in the conjugal family, the hazards of urban life force many women to work. If a male member of the rural extended family dies or is incapacitated, the women have other breadwinners, but such a loss in the urban conjugal family in an underdeveloped country forces into work any but an upper class woman. Mortality, sickness, high divorce rates, and frequent desertions produce many broken families in the slums of African, Middle Eastern, and Caribbean cities. The few available surveys show that many of the working women are self-supporting or are the breadwinners for broken homes.[27] Little research has been done on the reasons why members of nursing service work in underdeveloped countries, but the independent habits of mind and economic pressures arising from broken homes may be widespread. For example, a study of the thirty-two members of a class in professional nursing in Africa found that nine had lost their fathers, four were orphans, and seventeen had been brought up by persons other than their parents for at least two years.[28] Probably the incidence of broken families and disrupted marriages among practical nurses and auxiliaries is much higher, particularly in countries that are being detribalized and where *purdah* is being abandoned.

The newly established graduate nursing schools in countries of this type may attract some girls from stable urban or rural homes, since the schools prefer applicants who have had prior education and who can produce letters of recommendation. In a few countries, the Royal Family and other government leaders have become committed to health improvement policies and have realized that only their personal example would stimulate recruitment of adequately educated nurses. So, in Yemen, Brunei, Afghanistan, and Kuwait, some of the first students in newly established nursing schools were daughters sent by the Royal Family and by other elite families under royal influence.[29] This recruitment from the elite occurs when hospitalization of women preceded the opening of the nursing school only by a short period. A long tradition of nursing by unskilled lower class women is absent, and consequently upper class families and their daughters do not have an unfavorable image of nursing. Recruitment from the upper class presupposes a certain type of nursing work and personal regulation, as is discussed at greater length in the rest of this chapter. Parents assume that the daughters will have minimum contact with men, will do little dirty and dangerous work, will be guarded and regulated, and will be taught by trustworthy and prestigious European instructors.

Countries of moderate opportunity for the education and employment of women: nursing as a female occupation. In the aforementioned countries, the employment of women is governed very strictly by family obligations. The most approved and customary role is employment on the family farm or in the home. Low-income urban couples need the money women can earn. Some female employees are driven by economic necessity resulting from family breakups. Some daughters are assigned to jobs by their parents. Female employment will be forbidden among the economically secure classes if it jeopardizes the family's reputation.

Modernization makes other countries quite different. A larger female public labor force follows from industrialization, urbanization, the resulting change in family structure and the resulting stimulation of women's aspirations. Numerous women get a certain amount of primary education, and some get more. Many single and married women work in urban family business, such as shops, cafes, street peddling, and handicrafts. This transitional situation between the rural family economic unit and the urban economy accustoms both male and female family members to rational and functionally specific urban employment conditions and weakens traditional taboos about contact of women with strange men. Meanwhile, the expansion of urban commerce and industry provides job openings that are offered to women, either because enough men are not available for that type of work or because women work at lower cost. With the rise of family living expenses and aspirations and with the development of women's own consumption aspirations for clothing and other amenities, women will have a strong incentive for wage employment. The proportion of women in the total labor force may not increase, but many women may transfer from full-time or part-time work in the family enterprise into a more disciplined and more productive wage-paying job.

Cities throughout the world have experienced this evolution. It has affected more women in the West, because the latter experienced urbanization, industrialization, and mass public education first. This trend has been strongest in the West for religious and ideological reasons too. Judaism and Christianity have been among the most strongly emancipationist religions. Respect for women is very prominent throughout the Bible. The lone woman serving the public was commended by the New Testament and eventually became an important functionary of the Christian Church.[30] In addition, Christianity, both by its doctrine[31] and by the fact that it was the religion of European city dwellers, has encouraged the conjugal family and opposed the extended family. Consequently in comparison with the women of most societies with extended family systems, the Western girl has not grown up in an almost completely female personal environment, she has not been so completely controlled by older women, she has had more daily contact with men, and the smaller number of people around her has allowed more free time for her own thinking and activity.

Among the numerous occupations that women enter in such countries is nursing. Men tend to avoid nursing because of opportunities in the rest of the economy and because of the usual tendency in the world for men to avoid occupations stereotyped as female. Service work in each country is usually heavily male or heavily female; in all the developed and some of the urbanized underdeveloped countries it is primarily female,[32] and most hospital ranks usually become female. The taboo against women caring for men may never have existed in these countries; or it may be overcome and forgotten after several centuries of nursing by sexually neutral female religious (as in some parts of Europe); or it may be defied with resultant damage to the public reputation of nursing work (as in nineteenth-century England or twentieth-century Turkey).

Usually at the time of the mass female entry into nursing, hospital employees cannot offer much educational preparation, and hospital nursing work does not demand it. For example, nineteenth-century European hospitals and twentieth-century Middle Eastern urban hospitals during initial growth have hired numerous single or married working class girls between fourteen and twenty years old, with five or fewer years of primary schooling; they perform responsible nursing functions at once, may never receive formal training, and may constitute virtually the entire nursing staff. As more women become educated in the country and as hospital work becomes more difficult, the hospitals get some applicants with more education and may even introduce some training courses themselves. Therefore, a small number of graduate nurses will be superimposed upon a nursing service composed principally of many auxiliaries. The graduate nurses enter nursing school at about fifteen or sixteen after about eight years of primary school; length of training varies among these countries from two to five years. The untrained auxiliaries are hired from any applicants at the personnel office. Many auxiliaries are girls in their middle teens with about four years of primary school; others may be older, perhaps married, probably employed earlier in a series of nonmedical jobs. All members of nursing service tend to come from the large urban proletariat, and public opinion may stereotype nursing as a job appropriate for working class girls. The foregoing describes the personnel in nursing service in any of the public hospitals today in the large Middle Eastern cities (Istanbul, Ankara, Damascus, Bagdad, Alexandria, and Cairo) and in much of Latin America. Such was nursing personnel in much of Europe before World War I.

When professional education in nursing begins in such countries —as in England during Florence Nightingale's day and in Egypt and Turkey today—a great problem is the attraction of enough of the girls with the appropriate schooling and skills, when their upper class parents had developed the unfavorable stereotypes from the past. The first collegiate school of nursing in Turkey failed because secondary school graduates would not enter it.[33] Some doctors and hospital administrators, retaining the earlier stereotype based on uneducated and submissive women in the general labor force and in the hospital, may oppose attempts to upgrade the education, duties, and rank of hospital nurses to accommodate the new recruits. A few attempts to create collegiate schools of nursing in the Middle East and Asia have been vetoed by medical faculties who did not wish nursing to achieve parity in the university structure. The medical critics, whether of the nineteenth or twentieth centuries, usually object that higher educational prerequisites and more nursing education are unnecessary for the existing type of nursing service, and that such recruits would not fit into the hospital.[34]

In order to fill their new professional schools with better-educated upper class girls, the innovators redefine nursing work so the new professional nurse will seem more comparable to the pre-stigious schoolteacher, with less personal service and more administrative and technical tasks. Also, a public relations campaign is launched in order to raise the public image of nursing, applicants are screened, and parents are reassured by controls over the personal lives of students. Such were the tactics employed by Florence Nightingale and Sarah Wardroper during the creation of the St. Thomas' Hospital School of Nursing,[35] and they are emulated to-day in a more modern form by the new collegiate schools in Istanbul, Ankara, Alexandria, Delhi, and Manila.

Expansion of educational and occupational opportunities. As schools and jobs become more available to women, an increasing number enter the public labor market. More education upgrades the skills of the female labor force.

One would expect more numerous and more skilled recruits for nursing. Such trends have occurred in professional nursing in Europe and in America during the twentieth century. However, while the acceptance of female careers as "normal" increases the number interested in nursing, ceilings are created by the emergence of competing female career lines. The customary standards in modernized countries today are admission to graduate nursing school at the age of seventeen or eighteen, after ten to twelve years of earlier schooling.[36] Except for the few university-level schools of nursing, the field does not attract those who continue their liberal arts and professional education and who eventually enter schoolteaching and the professions.[37] The other alternatives to nursing school in the developed countries among those reaching this point in the preparatory educational ladder are immediate marriage and/or a job, either in an office or trade. Throughout Europe and America, nursing educators believe that these less burdensome and sometimes more remunerative office and trade occupations compete and reduce the maximum recruitment to nursing. (Perhaps this is true, but not enough research on career choice has been done to determine the number and types of entrants into graduate nursing if all other alternatives were shut.)

High recruitment into professional nursing can result from an inconsistent opportunity structure that produces a larger number of educated girls than the job market can absorb. This unusual situation exists in Eire. Many girls enter nursing because of this imbalance, the high prestige conferred by Catholic culture on nursing, and the economic need for many breadwinners in each Irish family. Consequently, Eire may have as many graduate nurses as it needs, and much of the bedside care is done by graduates rather than by auxiliaries. So many applications are submitted to nursing schools that they can charge tuition without creating the personnel shortages that would result in most other countries. Some believe the tuition fees make Irish nursing very select, by confining recruitment to the highly committed, the wealthier, and the better educated. Eire has the lowest marriage rate and the latest marriage age in the world. This situation and monopolization of supervisory nursing positions by nursing nuns would produce a crisis of overcrowding and blocked careers, but for the steady emigration of Irish nurses to England and other countries.[38]

The expansion of educational and occupational opportunities for women may create shortages at lower ranks in nursing, particularly among auxiliaries. Shortages have been growing throughout Europe, since the uneducated proletarian and rural women who once did this work are now diminishing in number and can find new alternatives. No research has been done on changes in recruitment and career choice, but many of my informants suspect that those women with more education than previous generations now enter skilled jobs in factories, shops, offices, and elsewhere, while those with no more education than before can find domestic or service jobs in hotels, restaurants, etc. Such alternative jobs may offer higher pay, shorter hours, lighter and cleaner work, and a less servile image. A few countries, such as the United States and the Republic of South Africa, can continue to recruit auxiliaries from subordinate races whose women do not participate in the growing opportunities.

Societies with maximum opportunities. In some countries women now have almost unlimited opportunities to get higher education and to enter professional and technical careers. Two examples are the Soviet Union and Poland. Women are expected to work, and they can enter higher education and the higher ranking occupations. The theme of strong and self-reliant women has long been prominent in literature. Wars and purges killed many men, and women constitute majorities of the adult population and of the labor force.

The result is serious shortages of able graduate nurses. In particular, medicine attracts the intelligent women who in other countries might have become the leaders in graduate nursing. Women constitute over half the medical school enrollments in both the U.S.S.R. and Poland; and this has been true so long in the Soviet Union that three-quarters of the doctors are women.[39]

The Soviet solution is to combine medicine and nursing in a single hierarchy characterized by degrees of education, skill, and responsibility. In contrast, the two occupations are separate in other countries, a woman must choose between nursing and medical careers, and nursing often seeks independent professional recognition and autonomy. Soviet women of limited education can enter secondary schools that train nurses or medical auxiliaries called *feldshers*. A few enter nursing temporarily because they lack the secondary education necessary for medical school, but once having secured the secondary certificate by this means, many then enter medical schools and become doctors. Nurses and feldshers are given priority over ordinary secondary school graduates if they tie on entrance examinations; nurses and feldshers comprise nearly half the student bodies of medical schools.[40] Of the one thousand nurses at a large Soviet hospital that I visited, about fifty quit nursing each year to become full-time students at a medical school; meanwhile other nurses were studying medicine in night courses. In part as a result of entry of the better educated and more vigorous women into medicine, Soviet nursing consists of bedside care rather than complex technical or administrative tasks, nurses and auxiliaries seem content to be the doctors' helpers, and there seem to be no pressures for independent nursing organization either within the hospital or in the country at large.[41]

Even if the family system and economy do not offer unlimited occupational opportunities for women in general, nursing recruitment may still suffer if opportunities are great in selected areas. For example, in some underdeveloped countries, *purdah* and other sex taboos produce a need for female doctors to treat women and children, and medicine is becoming a partly female profession. Many respondents in a survey of Moroccan women said they would prefer a female to a male doctor, and medicine was recommended more often than nursing as an ideal career for a woman.[42] As a result, some governments now actively recruit women for medicine and for other professions with female and child clienteles; since nursing is often stereotyped as an unskilled service, the small number of women with the necessary education are eager to pick medicine over nursing. One-quarter of the seats in first-year Pakistani medical school classes are reserved for women,[43] and consequently attempts to upgrade the educational standards and recruitment of Pakistani professional nursing have been handicapped by a shortage of the right kind of applicants.[44] Similarly, many Indian, Turkish, Indonesian, Thai, and Filipino women enter medicine with government encouragement, but this boomerangs against recruitment efforts by professional nursing leaders. Since the pool of educated women is so small in many underdeveloped countries, medicine and schoolteaching could easily absorb all of them, leaving none for nursing.[45] If the female sector in the medical profession of underdeveloped countries expands as fast as secondary education for women, then nursing will have recruitment problems for some time, and a ceiling will be placed on the technical and administrative skills that can be expected of it. Even at a lower level of skill, nursing might still be unable to recruit enough intelligent and vigorous women in competition with the more remunerative and more autonomous career of midwifery; in most underdeveloped countries today, midwifery already attracts many potential nurses, since midwifery school usually requires no more than primary school from entrants.[46]

Extensive admission of women into medicine has effects besides the immediate recruitment problems of hospitals. One result is the orientation of the feminist movements. Their leaders will have many relatives and class peers in medical school and in medical practice, but few in nursing. So, the feminist organizations will be far more interested in medicine than in nursing. For example, one of my Pakistani nursing informants complained that feminist leaders regularly made official visits to hospitals and medical schools to meet the "lady doctors" but always ignored the nurses. Similarly, in most of continental Europe, upper class girls can enter medicine, and my nursing informants complained that the feminist organizations usually ignored the nursing associations. In contrast, in England, America, and Finland, many educated and vigorous women entered nursing, their emancipationist energies involved them in the leaderships of both the nursing associations and the women's rights movements, and the two organizations often cooperated.[47]

Commitment to Nursing

The turnover and performance of nurses depends on the attitudes of the families as well as on the content of the work and the organization of the hospital. At first, hospitals alter the work and the organization of nursing service in order to attract suitable girls and diminish strains upon them. As societies modernize, adolescent girls become more independent of their families, and the hospitals' controls over them—originally designed to mollify the families—chafe and constitute new sources of strain. Eventually modernization of the hospital increases the technical and administrative content of the work of graduate nurses, both nurses and their families are more contented with the intellectual rewards and the image of the field, the nurses make better adjustments with patients and doctors, and the hospitals relax their controls.

Recruitment and initial adjustment of the student nurse. Whether entry into a nursing school involves strains for the student depends on whether her family status defines it as an upward or downward move. Nursing seems attractive to some groups in some countries, and parents seem to encourage daughters to enter: for example, in Eire and Finland it is a socially respected career; for many English working class girls it has been one of the few available channels to rise in the class structure;[48] in many underdeveloped countries, it is one of the few ways that an urban working class daughter or wife can supplement the family income substantially.

On the other hand, a great problem for health officials trying to upgrade nursing service is the hostility of upper class parents. In the Middle East, for example, upper class families that once practiced *purdah* are now willing to let their daughters attend universities, but employment is still discouraged if it jeopardizes the daughter's marriageability and the family's honor, or if it arouses the traditional connotation that any work by a woman is a sign that her father or husband is unsuccessful.

In much of the Middle East and Asia today, when an upper class girl indicates interest in nursing school, a family dispute ensues.[49] Nursing is perceived as a lower class job and nursing school puts the girl to work at the start rather than at the end, while arguments about other occupational choices can be postponed to the end of the educational phase. A century ago the same family disputes occurred when Florence Nightingale wished to enter and reorganize a lower class job.[50] A Druze instructor in a Middle Eastern nursing school told me of the same events, experienced today by herself and by many of her students:

Usually it is the girl who decides. She suggests it after graduation from high school. She may have had a friend in nursing or may have seen a hospital. First, the family usually opposes the idea—90 percent of the Muslim families would oppose it. Then the girl must stand up or bring in a friend to argue on her behalf. . . . Once they come here to school, they have usually conquered the family's opposition.

I had to pass through the same thing. I had to overcome my family, but after I came, I did not feel any strain. (How did you deal with your family's opposition?) I had a good friend in nursing whom I always point to. My brother was the one most opposed—brothers are often protectors of the sisters in Druze families, they uphold the honor of the male group in the family, and they are the guardians to see that sisters do not disgrace the brothers. My mother was favorable. The rest of the family did not approve, but they were not so obviously opposed as my brother. Gradually they accepted my going into nursing. But I still feel strange about being a nurse.

But not every family dispute is resolved amicably. Another informant described situations in one of the more conservative Muslim countries:

Some girls were ostracized by their families because they went into nursing. They had no place to go during vacations and stayed in the nursing school. In some families a brother came back from the army or from a long absence and protested when he found the sister was in nursing. Then the family would take the girl out of the nursing school.

If hospitals and female nursing have not antedated nursing education long enough for nursing to acquire an image of lower class membership and degrading personal service, the nursing school might not seem so objectionable to upper class families. For example, Kuwaiti and Yemeni nursing schools are the first form of secondary education open to girls and thus are profiting from the great respect conferred on all education during the early stage of economic growth. Attending the nursing school and working in the country's new hospitals are acceptable ways for higher status girls to get educated and learn the respected ways of the West. The hospitals become agencies for modernizing the position of women.

Sometimes parents can be mollified by manipulating the practice sites. For many years an Egyptian nursing school connected with a women's and children's hospital attracted more upper class students than the schools affiliated with general hospitals, where parents feared contact with men.[51] In Brunei, because hospital nursing by lower class women gave the field an adverse image, graduate nursing education had to begin in health centers and not in hospitals.[52]

Controls over personal life. If higher class women customarily do not work among strangers, and if nursing has been done heretofore by lower class women and has a public image of servility and physical intimacy, graduate nursing schools must institute controls over students as a condition for recruitment from upper class families. Into their early schools Florence Nightingale and her associates introduced a strict regime of hard work, study, long hours, prayers, chaperones, and accounting for all time, in order to convince upper class parents that their daughters were safe in a once disreputable occupation.[53] Besides reassuring families, the detailed controls and heavy work load were supposed to teach all necessary skills and instill total commitment to nursing as a way of life. Rigorous personal discipline, residence in hospital quarters, long work hours, and authoritarian relations at work continued throughout the nurse's career.[54]

In most countries, it was the individual hospital that controlled the lives and work of students and staff nurses. The individual could choose among hospitals or could take the financial risks of private practice, consisting of bedside care in homes. The Germanic countries developed lay associations (called *Mutterhäuser* or *Schwesternschäfte*) that resembled religious nursing orders. They trained, regulated, assigned, and supported the lay graduate nurse from the start of nursing school until retirement and death. Like the Nightingale system, the German corporative methods were supposed to protect the women, perform the hospital's work efficiently, and instill a conception of nursing as a spiritual vocation.[55]

Similar controls have been introduced by many of the new graduate nursing schools in Asia and the Middle East today, in order to reassure parents of potential students and to combat adverse public stereotypes of nursing. Parents may visit the school in advance, to be sure that the working schedule and supervisor are trustworthy, and to inspect the living quarters. Some schools have elaborate rules, in order to reassure the parents. A few forbid student nurses to talk to young doctors, even though this prevents educationally valuable shoptalk. A few years ago one of the Istanbul schools forbade students to look out the windows of the hospital. The Yemeni nursing school devised a special nurse's uniform that included a veil.[56] But recruitment of sheltered upper class girls and imposition of personal controls have permanent effects on the performance of nursing until families modernize: the student nurses cannot develop the self reliance and initiative expected by professional nursing in the modern hospital.[57]

In a few countries, such as the more conservative Muslim societies, a woman is not supposed to live away from relatives, since only relatives can be trusted to safeguard her. Therefore hospital residences cannot be created, nursing schools can be set up only in large cities, and they can recruit only girls from that locality. Students commute from home daily in buses provided by the school or in the company of relatives or fellow students. A strict schedule governs them in the school and hospital, while they follow their usual family routine during the evening, night, and weekends. They are day students and may lack training in night duty, emergency nursing, or public health home visiting. If continued, these practices would permanently bar recruitment from the villages where most of the population lives. But usually, after a few years, village families begin to trust the nursing school enough to send their daughters as resident students, provided the school regulates their conduct and brings them home on weekends.[58]

Personal controls usually linger after women in the society have become more free, after the public reputation of nursing has been raised, and after the model of religious nursing orders has become less compelling. A recurring controversy in every developed country is protest by nursing students and staff nurses that the controls appropriate for religious orders or for the sheltered daughters of worried parents are out of date, as other female college students and other employed women become more numerous and acquire more personal freedom.[59] Since the nursing school acts as a parental surrogate for resident students, it shares in the modern rebellion of daughters against parental restrictions. Familiar demands among professional nursing students and staff nurses throughout Europe today and in America in the recent past are increased free time in evenings and weekends, reduced working hours, the right to go on dates unescorted, the right to have male visitors in the recreation rooms of the nurses' residence, the right to smoke, and the right to chat with young doctors without eliciting scowls from the ward sister. Such changes have occurred rapidly in America, where leaders of professional nursing try to give the nursing student a status comparable to college undergraduates. Similar changes began in Europe after World War II and have accelerated as the rapid entry of women into higher schools and into competing careers made it necessary to increase the attractiveness of nursing, and as a new generation of American-oriented professional nurses became leaders.

The Effects of Sex Roles on Nursing Work

Sex-linked tasks. As has been previously discussed, taboos upon intimate contact with strangers of the opposite sex produce a sexual division of labor in nursing in some countries in Africa, the Middle East, and Asia. Male nurses will do all the nursing for male hospital patients, and female nurses for female patients. In hospitals in some Muslim countries, Western clinical instructors have tried to teach male and female students in a single group responsible for adjacent male and female wards in internal medicine and other specialties; but the male students usually do not relish the idea of serving a female patient, female students are often shy with male patients, and—in the absence of instructors' controls—the students have often gravitated to the patients of the same sex.

Where the taboos are relaxed sufficiently to allow women to staff the male wards, barriers may remain for any nursing that has overtones of physical intimacy. The female professional nurses will give medications and change dressings. Male auxiliaries will catheterize patients and shave them for surgery; either a male auxiliary or a member of the patient's family will wash him and carry bedpans and urinals. Sexual taboos concerning who gives bed baths are not a great complication, since bed baths are rare outside Western hospitals.

As a country and its hospitals modernize and as the content of nursing work becomes more technical, sex-linked barriers diminish. The nurse becomes a professional specialist, and relations with the patient are determined primarily by his malady rather than by his sex. There remains one aspect of nursing work that depends on the fact that the nurse is usually a woman, namely the provision of emotional comfort to the patient.

A common belief is that nursing is fundamentally an expressive role and thus is an extension of the female status.[60] Mothers and wives are said to perform expressive tasks in certain social relationships in all known societies,[61] girls are taught attitudes facilitating performance of these feminine roles, and the presence of nurses with such qualities is essential to attract patients away from their families and into the hospital.[62]

Female expressiveness seems to affect recruitment. A remarkably widespread empirical finding in questionnaire surveys in many different societies is that students in professional nursing schools select this field from strongly expressive motivations, such as sympathy for the unfortunate and the wish to help people.[63] But modern medical care aims at the physical recovery of patients as well as at their happiness. Hospitals throughout the world have difficulty accomplishing both goals. In the developed countries emotional drives may be dominant at entry into nursing school, but an important function of the school is to modify them so the neophyte is ready for practical work. Instrumental duties are learned, excessive emotional involvement with patients is controlled, and new professional career drives may be acquired.[64] The modern hospital also militates against giving sustained emotional support to individual patients. In order to treat the physical problems of large numbers of patients, it requires the nurses to perform many administrative and scientific tasks in a short time, and contacts with individual patients are fleeting.[65] The feedback from comparisons of expectations and performance are now producing two new trends: in several modernized countries, one encounters complaints by the public that hospitals neglect emotional therapy[66] and complaints by nurses that the organization of hospitals prevents them from performing the expressive tasks that were their principal career incentive.[67]

Countries differ in the degree of performance of expressive work by nursing employees. Perhaps the variations fit an inverted U-curve: the lowest rate of practice of humane bedside care and the greatest preoccupation with a succession of short administrative and technical tasks occur in the most modernized and the least modernized countries. In the most developed countries—and particularly in the United States—both graduate nurses and lower nursing ranks may have become so accustomed to the busy routine, administrative tasks, numerous clinical procedures, and the general hospital's rapid turnover of patients that sustained emotional support of the patient no longer becomes either a personal aim of the employee, a goal of the organization, or an expectation of the patient himself.[68]

Class differences, career aspirations, and the ubiquity of suffering restrict the nurses' capacities to perform expressive roles in the hospitals of less developed countries. The wards of public hospitals are full of lower class patients with little education and doubtful prognoses. Nursing work is usually stereotyped as menial, unclean, and suitable for lower class women. Therefore graduate nurses usually avoid extensive contact with patients and prefer the cleaner and more prestigious tasks of administration, dispensing medications, and teaching students.[69] The practical nurses and auxiliaries usually come from the lower classes themselves and often are inured to suffering by strangers (see Chapter 4). Even if the nursing staff were motivated to give patients sustained personal attention, the work tempo would prevent it: as in the most modern countries, there exists a severe shortage of staff. Therefore, just as at home, the patient in underdeveloped countries must rely on visits by family members for emotional support during hospitalization.

As societies modernize, the visits by family members are regulated more strictly and the administrators of hospitals and nursing schools attempt to instill in all ranks of nursing service a commitment to giving patients both personal care and emotional support. Therefore the hospital temporarily replaces the family in meeting the patient's needs.

But such a break with the society's family customs is not attempted everywhere. In many private clinics in Europe, a family member is admitted with the patient or has unlimited visiting privileges. Since the patient pays, he is granted discretion in choosing his care. Admission of a female relative along with the patient has become a regular and formalized part of Japan's modern hospitals. Bathing, feeding, and around-the-clock companionship are supposed to be provided only by a female relative, and a member of the female hospital nursing staff often is expected to do no more than scientific and administrative tasks. Sometimes the Japanese family hires a private duty nurse, called a *tsukisoi*, who behaves exactly like a family member and who (particularly in mental hospitals) is matched with patients according to similar personality traits. Needless to say, these traditional arrangements displease many advocates of administrative rationality and professional nursing, since they introduce into the hospital organization independent nursing functionaries who emphasize affective rather than technical performance.[70]

Technical level of work. The higher the education of nurses, the more technical and administrative work they are given. Thus the higher the general level of personal culture and formal education of women in a country, the greater the number and complexity of technical tasks that the doctors give the hospital nurse, and the less continuous the supervision over her. As countries modernize, delegations from the doctors increase.

Countries differ in the amount of physical labor that women generally are accustomed to do inside the house, on the family farm, and in outside jobs. Lifting heavy objects, carrying things long distances, scrubbing floors on their knees, and working in sometimes unpleasant surroundings may be taken for granted in many countries. Most rural and many urban women eat heartily and may become muscular. As a result, the nurses of all ranks of such countries may perform such tasks routinely. In countries where women generally admire delicacy and femininity or where they can rise into high administrative and professional careers, professional nurses and even practical nurses will avoid manual labor in favor of scientific, administrative, and other bedside tasks.

An example of such cross-national differences is Germany and neighboring countries. Until the Franco-Italian feminine ideal became the model for the postwar German teenager, the country's women were accustomed to considerable manual labor, and this is still evident among many rural and urban workers who are presently over forty. In the past, and even very recently, German professional nurses and auxiliaries have been accustomed to lift patients, sort laundry, carry heavy objects, wash floors and walls, and do many other domestic tasks. Some of the Confessional Nursing Associations continue to believe that these tasks are part of nursing and resist proposals for national petitions demanding that hospitals give this work exclusively to domestics and to male employees. In contrast, such heavy work is now rarely done by other Western European women, either in outside employment or in the hospital. Much of the hospital's domestic work was still given to the English student nurse long after it had become unfashionable among English women generally, and it became one of the principal reasons for wastage.[71]

But as the position of women follows modern trends, the character of nursing work changes. For example, feminine stylishness has become the mode for young German girls now, just as in the rest of Europe. New German nurses doubtless will prefer technical and clerical over manual tasks. Nursing schools that lag in making the adjustment will suffer recruitment problems, as in prewar England.

Marriage and Nursing

Western nursing as a career for the unmarried. During much of the history of the West, marriage and nursing were assumed to be mutually exclusive. In many countries for centuries much of the nursing was done by Catholic nuns and Protestant Deaconesses ruled by vows of chastity, dedicated totally to work and religion, and housed in the hospital. Lay nurses and auxiliaries in many countries were widows or vagabonds who worked in the hospital in order to have room and board. When the professionalization of nursing began, it did not have to turn to wives, since a pool of single women was available. Western Europe always has had a lower female marriage rate and a later marriage age than any other society.[72]

For many decades after its founding, lay professional nursing was incompatible with marriage. During the nineteenth and early twentieth centuries, the middle and upper classes of Europe and America considered any sort of employment outside the home inappropriate for a wife and mother. Florence Nightingale had intended nursing as a lifelong alternative to the arranged marriages of her day, and many hospitals forbade the employment of married graduate nurses. Even when the social and legal taboos against work by wives weakened in the rest of the economy, the long working hours, obligations for night and weekend duty, and obligations to live in the hospital residence reduced a single nurse's chances for successful courtship and prevented the employment of married women. Consequently in many Western countries until recently the decision to become a professional nurse also implied the decision for probable lifelong spinsterhood.[73]

But women's increased freedom, dating, and greater social experience in the West have made marriage more voluntary and more attractive to them. In most Western countries women's marriage rates have risen, their ages at first marriage have declined, and therefore the pool of single women has diminished.[74] Meanwhile women's wage employment opportunities have been increasing. But since the school-leaving age has been rising while the marriage rate has been growing, the expansion of the female wage-earning labor force has been possible only through a very steep increase in the paid employment of married women, a trend that seems permanent.[75]

The old dualism between career and marriage is rapidly dying, although, as social surveys repeatedly show, both working women and public opinion stress the priority of family obligations.[76] An interest in working is not the same as strong commitment to the content of work.[77] Surveys of adolescent girls and young women in America reveal life plans and occupational attitudes that may be repeated in other countries. Virtually all the Americans anticipate both marriage and work. They have definite preferences for work that is pleasant, that is reasonably remunerative, and that can be resigned when children come. A few are strongly committed to work and wish to develop skills and success in a particular field; but even most of these wish the work to be coordinated with family life. A young woman with a career commitment stronger than family interests is very unusual.[78]

Parallel developments have occurred in nursing, with a time lag. The urbanization of populations and the increasing interest in marriage have reduced recruitment of nursing nuns and Deaconesses and likewise would have drastically reduced entry into any vocation hindering marriage. The surveys of Western nursing students cited earlier now show that the old dichotomy between nursing and marriage is dead in their minds; all the respondents expect to marry. Meanwhile, as hospital beds multiplied, as medical care became more complex, and as public health nursing arose and grew, the demand for graduate nurses increased. Some countries began to encounter difficulty recruiting auxiliaries, because of competing opportunities, and this added to the nursing shortage. Surveys in several countries began to show that many professional nurses were no longer practicing due to marriage.[79]

The shortage of nurses during and after World War II caused

hospitals in nearly every Western country to repeal rules against employment of married women. Laws and customs against the employment of wives in other competing occupations had already been repealed or were being abandoned at the same time as those for nurses.[80] The differences in marriage rates and marriage ages between nurses and other women have steadily diminished during the twentieth century, probably in every Western country.[81]

In the West, the old dichotomy between marriage and nursing is dying out first at the lower ranks. The nurses at the higher ranks are more likely to be single, partly because they are older and embody the marital patterns of the past, partly because they are the most strongly committed to nursing as a way of life. For example, over three-fifths of American hospital staff nurses are now married, but only one-third of the administrators in hospital nursing service are.[82] Similar differences by rank exist in England, although the marriage rates at each rank are somewhat lower. About half of the English staff nurses, one-quarter of the ward sisters and sister tutors, and 6 percent of the matrons and assistant matrons are married.[83] As adverse customs and inconveniences diminish, the marriage rates for Western nurses will approach those of the general population and differences by rank will diminish. In modernizing countries where marriage rates are traditionally higher than in Western Europe and where wives' employment is taken for granted —such as the Soviet Union and Israel—one finds many married women among the higher nursing ranks.

Nursing and marriage outside the West. Europe has had a long tradition of female vocations and a number of unmarried adult women to fill them. But in the rest of the world, virtually all women marry, and the marriage age often is very young. Marriage ages have been rising recently, so that girls can use their adolescence for schooling. The unmarried adolescent student is now recognized as a legitimate status, but not the unmarried adult worker. Therefore if any Western female occupation is exported to other societies, usually it cannot secure recruits unless it is suited to married women.[84]

In some of the less conservative underdeveloped countries, husbands and public opinion allow wives to work, provided they are home at night. Thus many women have salaried and wage-earning jobs in southeast Asia. The attractions of an extra family wage eventually can overcome even traditional Arab beliefs in the sheltering of women.[85] Western visitors to some underdeveloped countries, accustomed to the earlier Western conception of the nurse as a single career woman, are sometimes surprised to find that most of the members of nursing service are married. Nursing administrators in these countries may welcome the employment of married nurses, since an occupation's status in public opinion cannot be high if its membership consists of unmarried girls.[86] Drawbacks, however, are frequent absenteeism, understaffing at night, and nervous tension because of the sometimes unstable lives led by working class husbands in the turbulent cities of underdeveloped countries.[87]

Since marriage is a matter of course for all, the public image of nursing may affect recruitment even more than in societies providing for unmarried career women. For example, it is believed that many Indian women avoid nursing because the occupation's poor reputation will jeopardize their chances of marrying someone of equal or higher social class, and marriage prospects cause anxiety among Indian nurses.[88]

Gradually mutual accommodations occur between the hospital organization and the family system. Mutual influence during modernization enables the hospital to contribute to changes in the family. Having learned modern knowledge and exercised responsibility in the hospital, the nurse expects to be treated as an equal by her husband and resists the authority of her mother-in-law.[89]

Coordination of marital and nursing routines. A great source of conflict between nursing and marriage in most countries has been the hospital's timetable, but the feedback process leads to changes. As hospital managements notice that recruitment and retention suffer under the old schedule and improve with revisions, the hospital reorganizes.

Western public hospitals traditionally have had their peak medical activity during the morning, the patients were once expected to nap during the afternoon, and patients were given nighttime medications and prepared for bed in the evening. Thus for many decades the graduate nurses began early and were particularly busy in the morning and evening. During the years of the seventy-hour work weeks, the graduate nurse arrived early, remained late and had one day off. When working hours were reduced, in most of the world they were taken from the midday period when patients presumably were napping: the nurse might work from about 7 A.M. to noon, spend the next few hours in her room in the nurses' residence nearby, resume from about 3 P.M. to about 8 P.M., and spend the night in her room. She might be on call during her hours off duty; in some English hospitals as late as World War II, such as St. George's in London, the ward sister lived in a small apartment adjacent to her ward so that she would be available at all times.

The split shift, being on call, night duty, and weekend duty make hospital nursing difficult to coordinate with marriage, since the nurse is at work during hours when her husband is at home and when housework must be done. By repealing the rules banning the employment of married nurses, hospitals automatically relieved married nurses from the obligation to live in the nurse's residence and to be on call at night; as the system of adequate night shifts spread throughout the world, hospitals relieved single nurses, too, of the nighttime obligation. But split shifts, rotation on night duty and periodic weekend duty seemed inherent in hospital work organization and have been re-examined only because of the shortage of nurses. Throughout America and Europe many married nurses quit work completely or transferred from the hospital to nursing jobs whose work days and work weeks fit those of their husbands, such as public health, occupational health, nursing schools, or private office nursing.[90]

Therefore as the marriage rate of nurses rose, in nearly every country it seemed that the hospital nursing shortage would grow, particularly among the professional nurses possessing the greatest experience and value. Conversely, the higher marriage rate would help recruitment to other specialties, such as public health, in countries where such transfers are possible.

Throughout the world, one quick response of hospitals since World War II was replacement of the split shift with a continuous shift differing from that of other female occupations only in that it started and ended one or two hours earlier.[91] In many countries it had already been in effect before World War II for the auxiliaries, who had high marriage rates and who would not have accepted such jobs otherwise.

Whether to attract the married nurse by other scheduling concessions is one of the principal dilemmas of hospital administrators throughout the world today. Left to choose freely, every nurse —whether married or single—would work only on weekdays, would avoid night duty, and would take her vacation in August. The dilemma of hospital administrators nearly everywhere is that the higher the proportion of their nurses who are married, the greater the burden on the single nurses resulting from any preferential treatment for the married nurses, since the few single nurses will have all the night and weekend duty; but, on the other hand, the fewer the concessions granted the married nurses, the greater the attrition in their staffs. In practice, vacations are usually given at the same time as the husbands', but most of the hospital administrators I met expect the married nurses without children to work the same shifts as the unmarried, as often do the nurses themselves when polled.[92]

In many Western countries, part-time nursing jobs have developed rapidly in recent years, particularly among the lower ranks of nursing service. In the English National Health Service now, one-fifth of the graduate nurses, over one-third of the practical nurses, and nearly half the auxiliaries are part-timers,[93] a far cry from the round-the-clock vocation of the Nightingale period. Over two-fifths of American hospital general duty nurses are now part-timers, and perhaps most student nurses expect to be working part time within a few years of graduation.[94] This is part of a trend throughout the Western labor force. Economic need and a desire to keep busy create a large demand for part-time jobs whenever they are available to women. Although the religious orders and the reformers of the Nightingale period assumed that nursing could not be done except on a round-the-clock basis, the hospital is one of the settings best suited to part-time workers, since its daily schedule is periodic and personnel can be moved around the organization. Other work sites, such as factories, are not as well suited for part-time work, since a constant group of people must work at a steady tempo in fixed places.[95] Few underdeveloped countries have established part-time nursing yet, but only because professional nursing still is too new to have numerous retired mothers, and because hospitals and jobs are still too few for administrators to sense that the pool of single women and newlyweds will be insufficient. Probably in the future in all countries (but for a few exceptions like Eire) the typical nurse will be a wife (and often a mother), hospital organization will become adapted to the use and coordination of part-time jobs, and nursing service will consist of many part-timers (chiefly mothers) working under a few full-timers (many of them married women without children).[96]

Motherhood. To be a wife differs from being a mother, and employment of each has followed different national conceptions of family duty. In many countries, wives could work for pay but would drop out of employment permanently upon pregnancy. But social norms about work by mothers are changing rapidly now.

In countries where many mothers work for pay, two principal types of employment history are developing. Middle class white women in the United States now follow a definite cycle: they work up to the birth of the first child in order to save money; they care for the children until the last one enters nursery school; and they resume part-time work in order to avoid boredom and supplement the family's income.[97] The utilization of education and skills in an interesting way is at least as important as economic need, as evidenced by the recent reversal of the former inverse correlation between family income and employment rate.[98] Many American graduate nurses follow this trend toward part-time work by educated mothers.[99] For example, a survey of the graduates of a large American nursing school found that 79 percent marry within the first year after graduation, most have had one child and have quit nursing within three years of graduation, and many eventually resume as hospital staff nurses.[100] Many American hospitals could not operate without nurse–mothers and therefore provide crèches.[101]

Possibly this cycle will become widespread in the world for two reasons: first, the lowering of the marriage age (in the West), the smaller family, and greater longevity will reduce the life span devoted to child care and will increase the number of unoccupied adult years; second, better education for women will cause more to become bored by housekeeping. The changes in age, family size, and longevity are occurring in many developed countries today and are believed to be contributing to the start of a cyclical pattern in wives' employment.[102] Incentives to work arising from better education are beginning to appear in surveys of middle class mothers in some of the developed countries; some now resume work in order to lead an interesting life and buy extra amenities.[103] As yet only nursing in America is clearly included in this cycle, but probably the pattern will spread as foreign hospitals reduce their reliance on students, adapt their work schedules to the convenience of mothers, and begin installing crèches. Signs of changing times are already evident. Some new English hospitals without training schools to provide student labor now are staffed by married nurses and auxiliaries, mostly working part time.[104]

The second type of work by mothers is continuous rather than cyclical; nurses and other women work steadily with only short intervals for child-bearing. Hospitals do not adapt themselves in order to attract mothers back by such concessions as numerous part-time jobs, since all women customarily work normal shifts. A present example is Russia, and much of Eastern Europe may be developing the same pattern. Family incomes often would be inadequate without the wife's contribution, all women normally work, and pressures to stay home are fewer than in other countries—apartments, particularly in the Soviet Union, are too small to provide much housework; a grandmother often lives with the couple, cares for the children, queues up at the food shops, and does much of the cooking; the municipality and many hospitals provide crèches and schools that care for the child during the mother's work.[105] The customary urban timetables in the U.S.S.R. and some other Eastern European countries make it much easier for mothers to work than elsewhere in Europe—everyone starts around 8 A.M. or 9 A.M. and works until midafternoon without a luncheon break; mothers do not lose time because of midday travelling and have work hours corresponding identically with children's school hours. Mothers work night shifts in nursing service by normal rotation, as in any other occupation.

Effects of marriage and motherhood on nursing work. Surveys of female blue-collar and white-collar workers in several Western countries have shown that, although jobs are welcomed, they are given lower priority than competing family obligations: in comparison with men, wives (particularly young wives) seem to have lower interest in work, higher sick and voluntary absenteeism, more turnover, and less eagerness for promotions requiring greater responsibilities.[106] American data suggest that older married women without children and with uninterrupted careers have stronger work commitments than mothers, and possibly this is true in other countries too.

Married nurses, particularly those with children, likewise are more strongly committed to their families. Both students and graduate nurses in the United States tell interviewers that marriage and children seem more important than nursing, that these factors would cause many to drop out of school and out of practice, and that these factors would cause changes of jobs.[107] Commitment toward nursing is higher than toward any alternative occupation, but it is weaker than the tug of family. Nimkoff's survey of marital adjustment in a small sample of American graduate nurses suggests that successful home life may inhibit professional ambition; married matrons and ward sisters had lower adjustment scores than staff nurses and public health nurses.[108] Even in the countries where public opinion emphasizes women's occupational responsibilities and where female employment is continuous rather than cyclical, maternal roles still are considered superior by both the mothers and the hospital administration. For example, in both Poland and Russia, nurse–mothers can stay home to care for sick children, and they try to get jobs in hospitals close to their apartments. In Moscow, the housing boom has unexpectedly produced some turnover among hospital nurses, as they switch jobs to sites closer to their new apartments.

The social structure of the hospital is transformed when many wives and mothers enter a social system previously organized to cope with full-time, more submissive, and more committed single women. Instability and discontinuities are beginning to characterize some English and American nursing services because so many of their members have short shifts, high turnover, frequent absences, and weekday schedules.[109] The rank structure, long the basis of English nursing organization, can no longer control or motivate the new part-timers and is sometimes abandoned; because being a wife and mother is more important than being a nurse, the part-timers don't care whether they are ward sisters or staff nurses.[110] The rise in the marriage rate among British nurses has led to a decline in the number of applications for posts with higher responsibility.[111] Similarly, nearly half the married American graduate nurses interviewed by Corwin said they would refuse a promotion, but less than one-fifth of the unmarried nurses said this.[112] Rank and experience no longer correlate: often the part-time married staff nurse is older, has worked longer, and has had greater responsibilities than the full-time ward sister.[113] The authoritarianism once practiced by British matrons and ward sisters toward unmarried staff nurses is now being replaced by the more adaptable and egalitarian approach necessary to keep married staff nurses from quitting or from complaining to the Ministry of Social Security.

Summary

Following are the principal family variables used in the chapter:

B.1 Family care in the home
B.2 Family care away from home
B.3 Sheltering of women
    B.3.1 Differentials in sheltering by class
B.4 Instability of families
B.5 Education of women
B.6 Opportunities for women in professions
B.7 Expectation that women play expressive roles
B.8 Marriage age for women
B.9 Marriage rate for women

Following are the principal propositions derived from this chapter. The list of dependent variables about hospital organizations appears at the end of Chapter 1 (pp. 10–11).

The more widespread is family care of sick members in the home (B.1), then:

The lower the utilization of hospitals, particularly in patient services (1.4 and 1.5)
The smaller the number of hospitals (5.4)
The smaller the sizes of hospitals (2.1)
The smaller the proportion of women employees (1.1.3)

The more widespread is family care of sick members in the hospital (B.2), then:

> The smaller the nursing and housekeeping staffs (2.3.2 and 2.3.4)
> The graduate nurses specialize in clinical and related administrative work (4.1)
> The weaker the controls over patients (3.6)
> The greater the responsiveness to the patient's conception of treatment (4.13)

The more thorough the sheltering of women (B.3), then:

> The smaller the proportion of women patients (1.4.1 and 1.5.1)
> The lower the proportion of obstetrical and gynecological cases in the work load (6.3)
> The smaller the proportion of women employees (1.1.3)
> The smaller the number of hospitals (5.4)
> The smaller the sizes of hospitals (2.1)
> The greater the conflicting demands by the female employee's non-medical social statuses (4.8)
> The lower the female employee's priorities given to work (4.7)
> The lower the discretion given to female employees (3.5)
> The closer the controls over female employees (3.6)

Where sheltering of women is greater in the upper than in the lower classes (B.3.1), then:

> The lower the skills of female employees (1.1.2 and 1.1.3)
> The larger the proportion of auxiliaries in nursing service (2.3.2 and 2.3.3)
> The more class-bound the utilization of each hospital—i.e., upper classes use private clinics and avoid public hospitals (1.5.2)
> Graduate nurses concentrate on clinical and administrative work, and they avoid bedside chores and housekeeping (4.1 and 4.2)
> The more authoritarian are relations between graduate nurses and auxiliaries (3.5 and 3.6)

The more unstable a society's family life, particularly by deaths and desertions (B.4), then:

> The easier the recruitment of nurses (1.1.1)
> The lower the skills of nurses (1.1.2)

The higher the education for women (B.5) and the lower their professional opportunities (B.6), then:

The greater the recruitment into nursing (1.1.1)
The more complex the work of nurses (4.10)
The greater the nurses' resistance to authoritarian control (3.6)
The greater the nurses' demands for discretion (3.5)
The greater the nurses' demands to share in hospital policy-making (3.4)

The higher the education for women (B.5) and the greater their professional opportunities (B.6), then:

The lower the recruitment of skilled women into nursing (1.1.2)
The less complex the work of nurses (4.10)
The more authoritarian the controls over nurses, and the fewer delegations of work by doctors (3.5 and 3.6)

The greater the cultural expectation that women play expressive roles (B.7), then:

The stronger the expressive motives for employment (1.1.4)
The lower the satisfaction by nurses and the public over the nature of their work (4.11)

The later the marriage age for women (B.8) and/or the lower the marriage rate for women (B.9), then:

The greater the importance of religious motivations in recruitment (1.1.4)
The more authoritarian the structure of nursing service (3.5 and 3.6)
The greater the number of housekeeping tasks by nurses (4.2)
The longer the work hours (4.9)
The greater the priorities given to work (4.7)
The stronger the effects of rewards for assuming higher responsibilities (4.11.2)
The more clear the hierarchy of ranks (2.4)

Notes

1. On the ubiquity of healers in all societies, see W. H. R. Rivers, *Medicine, Magic, and Religion* (London: Kegan Paul, Trench, Trubner and Co., 1924), p. 5; William Caudill, "Applied Anthropology in Medicine," in A. L. Kroeber (ed.), *Anthropology Today* (Chicago: The University of Chicago Press, 1953), p. 772; and D. B. Jelliffe and F. J. Bennett, "Indigenous Medical Systems and Child Health,"

The Journal of Pediatrics, 57:2 (August 1960), 252-256. On the prominent role of the family in caring for the patient and in mediating between him and the healers, see Margaret Read, *Culture, Health, and Disease* (London: Tavistock Publications, 1966), Ch. 2.

2. P. Huard, "Les médecines africaines populaires," *Le concours médical*, 81:9 (28 February 1959), 967.

3. Naomi Mitchison, "Two Egyptian Hospitals," *Medical World*, 93:2 (August 1960), 146-148; Ahmed Kamel Mazen, "Development of the Medical Care Program of the Egyptian Region of the United Arab Republic" (Stanford: unpublished dissertation for the Ph.D. in Medical Care Administration, Stanford University, 1961), 49-50; Eugene Schoenfeld, "A Summer at Dr. Schweitzer's Hospital," *The Journal of Medical Education*, 36:3 (March 1961), pp. 223-226; and James Kennedy, "Bygones of a Bundu Bone Thrower," *The Central African Journal of Medicine*, 3:6 (June 1957), 239-240.

4. E.g., Janet Welch, *Nursing Related to the Cultural Background in East and Southeast African Colonies* (New York: King's Crown Press, 1941), p. 62, and T. Adeoye Lambo, "Mental Health in Africa," *Medical World*, 95:3 (September 1961), 198-202. Some of these hospitals specialize in maternity care. The women would resist inpatient hospitalization but are willing to live with their relatives and their other children in "maternity villages" while awaiting delivery. Normally they are delivered by the staff midwives in the huts. But they can be taken to the inpatient beds or operating theater if necessary. Maurice King (ed.), *Medical Care in Developing Countries* (Nairobi: Oxford University Press, 1966), Sec. 19:6.

5. For a survey of thirty-two developed and underdeveloped countries concerning the role of family members as visitors or as active members of nursing service, see Frances S. Beck, "The Family's Part in Caring for the Patient," *International Nursing Review*, 12:1 (February 1965), 31-50. For descriptions of hospital wards where the families give bedside nursing, see C. R. M. Prentice, "The Land of the Million Elephants—Two Years with a Medical Team in Laos," *The Lancet*, 10 August 1963, pp. 289-292; Ernestine Friedl, "Hospital Care in Provincial Greece," *Human Organization*, 16:4 (1958), 24-27; Infirmarius, "Hospitals in Central Africa," *The Hospital*, 56:10 (October 1960), 839; Robert C. Stever, "Medical Impressions from India and Nepal," *The Journal of Medical Education*, 36:4 (April 1961), 332; Jane C. Wright, "A Survey of Medical Conditions in Ghana in 1957," *Journal of the National Medical Association*, 53:4 (July 1961), 314; and Kennedy, "Bygones of a Bundu Bone Thrower," p. 240.

6. E. C. Jali, "Magic and Witchcraft in the Hospital Ward," in *African Culture and Its Relation to the Training of African Nurses* (Johannesburg: Transvaal Nursing Education Discussion Group, South African Nursing Association, 1954); and D. B. Jelliffe, "The Organisation of MCH Services in Developing Regions: Hospital Services for Children," *The Journal of Tropical Pediatrics*, 13:1 (March 1967), 42-43.

7. Cicely D. Williams, "Maternal and Child Health in Kumasi in 1935," *The Journal of Tropical Pediatrics*, 2:3 (December 1956), 143-144; and Beck, "The

Family's Part in Caring for the Patient," pp. 43–50.

8. E. Kahn, S. Wayburne, and M. Fouche, "The Baragwanath Premature Baby Unit," *South African Medical Journal*, 28:22 (29 May 1954), 453–456; Vojin Matic, "A Hospital Without Nurses," *World Mental Health*, 9:3 (August 1957), 119–121; A. L. Thomas and I. D. Thomas, "Medical Impressions of Ghana, West Africa," *Journal of Medical Education*, 36:6 (June 1961), 698; Cicely D. Williams and J. W. Scharff, *An Experiment in Health Work in Trengganu, Malaya* (Beirut: School of Public Health, American University, 1960), p. 37; and Welch, *Nursing Related to the Cultural Background*, p. 62.

9. Edwin L. Crosby, "Observations on Japanese Hospitals," *Hospitals*, 31:15, Part 1 (August 1, 1957), 35–36.

10. Alice Wilkinson, *A Brief History of Nursing in India and Pakistan* (Delhi: The Trained Nurses' Association of India, 1958), pp. 39–48.

11. Such increased use of hospitals in Ecuador is described in Charles J. Erasmus, *Man Takes Control: Cultural Development and American Aid* (Minneapolis: University of Minnesota Press, 1961), p. 29.

12. William J. Goode, *World Revolution and Family Patterns* (New York: The Free Press, 1963), Conclusion.

13. E.g., compare Frank G. Dickinson, *Age and Sex Distribution of Hospital Patients* (Chicago: American Medical Association, 1955); Brian Abel-Smith and Richard M. Titmuss, *The Cost of the National Health Service in Wales* (Cambridge: The University Press, 1956), p. 141; Robert F. Bridgman, *L'hôpital et la cité* (Paris: Éditions du Cosmos, 1963), p. 176; and J. Fehler, "Verweildauer im Allgemeinen Krankenhaus," *Das Krankenhaus*, 53:9 (September 1961), 397–403; with the Egyptian data in Ahmed Kamel Mazen, "Development of the Medical Care Program of the Egyptian Region of the United Arab Republic" (Stanford, Calif.: unpublished dissertation for the Ph.D. in Medical Care Administration, Stanford University, 1961), pp. 213–214; and with the Colombian data in Robert F. L. Logan, "International Studies of Illness and Health Services," *The Milbank Memorial Fund Quarterly*, 46:2, Part 2 (April 1968), 137–138.

14. "Women in the Labour Force," *International Labour Review*, 77:3 (March 1958), 254–272; Andrew Collver and Eleanor Langlois, "The Female Labor Force in Metropolitan Areas: An International Comparison," *Economic Development and Cultural Change*, 10:4 (July 1962), 367–385, and *Demographic Aspects of Manpower: Sex and Age Patterns of Participation in Economic Activities* (New York: Bureau of Social Affairs, Population Branch, The United Nations, 1962).

15. E.g., Delores Schemmel, "An Approach to Nursing Education" (Beirut: unpublished paper presented to the Eighth Middle East Medical Assembly, 1958).

16. Clement C. Chesterman, "The Training and Employment of Auxiliary Personnel in Medical and Health Services in Tropical Africa," *The Journal of Tropical Medicine and Hygiene*, 56 (June 1953), 127–129.

17. E.g., compare the favorable attitudes of Indian male nurses reported by Pauline Estelle King, "Potential Use of Nurses in Primary Health Centers in Madras State, India" (New York: unpublished dissertation for the Ed.D. in Nursing Education, Columbia University, 1962), Ch. 6, pp. 5–7, with the English and French situations described by Brian Watkin, "Present Position of Male Nurses in Hospital," *Nursing Mirror,* 108 (May 1 and May 15, 1959), 353–354 and 519–520; Gertrude A. Ramsden, *The Work of Recently Qualified Nurses* (London: Dan Mason Nursing Research Committee, 1956), pp. 23–32; Gertrude A. Ramsden, *The Work, Responsibilities and Status of the Staff Nurse* (London: Dan Mason Nursing Research Committee, 1960), pp. 47 and 54; and A. Montesinos, "Les infirmiers et la profession en France," *Revue de l'infirmière et de l'assistante sociale,* 12:5 (May 1962), 267–272.

18. E.g., Prentice, "Million Elephants," pp. 291–292.

19. Chesterman, "Auxiliary Personnel."

20. Naguib Mahfouz, *The History of Medical Education in Egypt* (Cairo: Government Press, Bulaq, 1935), pp. 71–72.

21. Helena F. Reimer, "The Role of Women and the Development of Nursing in Modern Egypt" (Chicago: unpublished thesis for the M.A. in the Social Sciences, University of Chicago, 1957), pp. 35–56.

22. Foreign visitors to African and conservative Muslim countries often are surprised to find that most of the hospital nurses are men; their image of a female nursing service had been formed by Europe and America. But in Africa and much of Asia, as I have said, the women are recent entrants into a formerly male occupation. Often the male members of nursing service have had more education than the female members. D. F. McCarthy, "Afghan Interlude," *Journal of the Irish Medical Association,* 36:212 (February 1955), 33; A. W. Williams, "The History of Mulago Hospital and the Makarere College Medical School," *East African Medical Journal,* 29 (July 1952), 260; Elizabeth Colmers, "Nursing Education in Some African Territories," *Nursing Outlook,* 1:8 (August 1953), 466–467; Lyle Creelman, "Nursing in the African Region," *International Nursing Review,* 5:2 (April 1958), 20; A. L. Thomas and I. D. Thomas, "Medical Impressions of Ghana, West Africa," *Journal of Medical Education,* 36:6 (June 1961), 698. Until the twentieth century, nursing in much of continental Europe was divided between men and women for many of the same reasons. Henry C. Burdett, *Hospitals and Asylums of the World* (London: J. & A. Churchill, 1893), Vol. III, Chs. 17–29 passim.

23. Alice Wilkinson, *A Brief History of Nursing in India and Pakistan* (Delhi: The Trained Nurses' Association of India, 1958), Ch. 5.

24. Gideon Sjoberg, *The Preindustrial City* (Glencoe: The Free Press, 1960), pp. 148, 157–162, and 169.

25. Georges Balandier, *Sociologie des Brazzavilles noirs* (Paris: Librairie Armand Colin, 1955), pp. 126–137 and 192–198; and Marie-Hélène Lefaucheux, "The Contribution of Women to the Economic and Social Development of African Coun-

tries," *International Labour Review*, 86:1 (July 1962), 20–21. Because the African communities in the Republic of South Africa lack *purdah* and since nursing is one of the best-paid jobs for women, working class fathers and relatives think nursing is one of the best careers for girls, according to the survey reported in Sheila T. Van der Horst, *African Workers in Town* (Cape Town: Oxford University Press, 1964), p. 125.

26. "Women's Employment in Asian Countries," *International Labour Review*, 68:3 (September 1953), 303–318.

27. E.g., Nelly Forget, "Attitudes towards Work by Women in Morocco," *International Social Science Journal*, 14:1 (1962), 115–116; Egbert de Vries, *Man in Rapid Social Change* (Garden City, N.Y.: Doubleday, 1961), p. 115; and Andrew Collver and Eleanor Langlois, "The Female Labor Force in Metropolitan Areas: An International Comparison," *Economic Development and Cultural Change*, 10:4 (July 1962), 375.

28. E. W. Peterson, "African Nurse Training—Ten Years of Progress," *Medical Proceedings*, 4:10 (17 May 1958), 329.

29. Ritchie Calder, *Ten Steps Forward* (Geneva: World Health Organization, 1958), pp. 8–9.

30. *Rom.*, XVI: 1–2. See Leopold Zscharnak, *Der dienst der Frau in den ersten Jahrhunderten der christlichen Kirche* (Göttingen: Vandenhoeck & Ruprecht, 1902); and Adelaide M. Nutting and Lavinia L. Dock, *A History of Nursing* (New York: Putnam, 1907), Vol. I, pp. 95–117. For centuries, the Church experienced controversies over whether female religious orders should be cloistered or might work among the public. At times apostolic work was forbidden as both profane and threatening to the women, but the bans were enforced unevenly, and "congregations" under looser ecclesiastic controls continued to nurse. After the sixteenth century, religious nursing orders evolved and were approved. Léon Joseph Cardinal Suenens, *The Nun in the World* (Westminster, Md.: The Newman Press, 2nd ed., 1963), pp. 36–40.

31. E.g., *Matt.*, XIX:5.

32. "Women in the Labour Force," pp. 271–272.

33. Eugenia K. Spalding, *Report of the Educational Survey Preliminary to Establishment of the Florence Nightingale Higher Educational Program for Nursing, Istanbul, Turkey* (New York: Teachers College, Columbia University, 1960), p. 48.

34. Cecil Woodham-Smith, *Florence Nightingale, 1820–1910* (New York: McGraw-Hill, 1951), p. 233; Nutting and Dock, *History of Nursing*, Vol. III, p. 316; Thomas Hale, Jr., "Why the Nursing Supply Is Failing to Meet the Demand," *The Modern Hospital*, 95:3 (September 1960), 100–104 and 130; Irwin Deutscher, *The Evaluation of Nurses by Male Physicians* (Kansas City: Community Studies, 1955), pp. 8 and 20–23; and Spalding, *Report of the Educational Survey*, pp. 41–42 and 139.

35. Lucy R. Seymer, *Florence Nightingale's Nurses: The Nightingale Training School, 1860–1960* (London: Pitman Publishing Company, 1960), pp. 19, 21–22, 44, 52–53, and 59–60.

36. *National Reports of Member Associations* (London: International Council of Nurses, 1961).

37. For example, nursing is no longer stereotyped as a lower class trade in Brazil, and parents pose fewer objections to the choice of nursing. But meanwhile opportunities for women are rising in the university, parents encourage professional careers, and therefore recruitment into nursing remains low. Glete de Alcantara, "Obstacles in Brazilian Society to the Expansion of the Nursing Profession," *International Nursing Review*, 11:3 (June 1964), 12–14.

38. On the numbers and work of nurses, see M. C. Prunty, "Is There a Real Shortage of Nurses: Ireland," *International Nursing Review*, 5:4 (October 1958), 23–25. On marriage and migration, see John A. O'Brien, *The Vanishing Irish* (New York: McGraw-Hill, 1958), pp. 163–164.

39. B. D. Petrov, "Le rôle des femmes dans le service de santé de l'U.R.S.S.," *Le concours médical*, 87:11 (13 March 1965), 1899–1900; and Jerzy Urban, "Medycyna pod Szpilka," *Polityka*, 6:26 (30 June 1962), 1–3.

40. For example, the Ukrainian statistics summarized by A. Plichet, "Les étudiants de médecine en U.R.S.S.," *La presse médicale*, 49 (20 May 1961), 1105.

41. E. D. Ashurkov, "The Work and Training of Feldshers and Nurses in the USSR," *Aspects of Public Health Nursing* (Geneva: World Health Organization, 1961), pp. 160–162; and J. J. Prewett, "Nursing and Medical Services in the Soviet Union," *Nursing Mirror*, 103 (6 April 1958), v-vii.

42. Forget, "Attitudes Towards Work," pp. 101 and 104.

43. *Women's Role in the Development of Tropical and Sub-Tropical Countries* (Brussels: International Institute of Differing Civilizations, 1959), p. 268.

44. Kaniz Mowla, "Progress in Pakistan," *The American Journal of Nursing*, 58:2 (February 1958), 237 and 239; John E. Owen, "Nursing in Pakistan," *Nursing Times*, 57:12 (24 March 1961), 378; and Ruth Woodsmall, *Women and the New East* (Washington: The Middle East Institute, 1960), pp. 114–119.

45. Mowla, "Progress in Pakistan," p. 237.

46. Woodsmall, *Women and the New East* pp. 114–115 and 210–211.

47. Genevieve Rogge Meyer, *Tenderness and Technique: Nursing Values in Transition* (Los Angeles: Institute of Industrial Relations, University of California, 1960), p. 5

48. Kathleen Box and Enid Croft-White, *Recruitment to Nursing* (London: The Social Survey, 1943), pp. 7–14 passim.

49. E.g., L. M. Thapalyal and T. S. Satyan, "Kulwinder from India," *World Health*, December 1963, pp. 10–13.

50. Woodham-Smith, *Florence Nightingale*, pp. 38, 52, 57, 60 and 65–73.

51. Reimer, "Women and Nursing in Modern Egypt," pp. 73–74.

52. Calder, *Ten Steps Forward*, pp. 9–10.

53. Seymer, *Florence Nightingale's Nurses*, pp. 34–35, 68, 73–74, 97, 157, and 166.

54. These conditions remained until shortly after World War II in the developed countries. A description of the British situation is in Lancet Commission on Nursing, *Final Report* (London: The Lancet, 1932).

55. Anton Ehl, *Die Ordensschwestern im Krankendienst* (Freiburg: Caritas Verlag, 1921); Georg Streiter, *Die wirtschaftliche und soziale Lage der beruflichen Krankenpflege in Deutschland* (Jena: Gustav Fischer, 2nd ed., 1924); and "Rechtsschutz für die Haube," *Der Spiegel*, 11:26 (26 June 1957), 18–26. The kind of lay nurse that these confessional and Red Cross schools have tried to develop is described in Marcelle Dalloni, *Sous les armes de la charité: aux infirmières* (Fribourg: Éditions de l'Imprimerie St.-Paul, 3rd ed., 1950).

56. Photographs in Germaine Tillion, "Women Emerge from the Shadows," *World Health*, May–June 1962, p. 31; in "Veiled Pioneers Join Health Drive," *International Nursing Review*, 10:3 (May–June 1963), 53; and on the Yemeni postage stamps publicizing maternal and child health.

57. The effects in prewar Thailand are described in Alice Fitzgerald, "Western Influence on Nursing Education in the Orient," *International Aspects of Nursing Education* (New York: Bureau of Publications, Teachers College, 1932), p. 131.

58. E.g., Gordon Boshell, "Afghanistan: How Ziagul Became a Nurse," *World Health*, January–February 1961, pp. 14–15.

59. E.g., Sheila Bevington, *Nursing Life and Discipline* (London: Lewis, 1943), pp. 22–24; Brian Abel-Smith, *A History of the Nursing Profession* (London: Heinemann, 1960), pp. 139–142; and *Denkschrift zur Lage des Krankenpflegeberufes in der Bundesrepublik Deutschland* (Hannover: Agnes Karll-Verband, 1958), pp. 4–7 passim.

60. This hypothesis has been argued by several sociologists, notably Johann Rohde, *Soziologie des Krankenhauses* (Stuttgart: Ferdinand Enke Verlag, 1962), pp. 284–289; George Devereux and Florence R. Weiner, "The Occupational Status of Nurses," *American Sociological Review*, 15:5 (October 1950), 628–634; Isador Thorner, "Nursing: Functional Significance of an Institutional Pattern," *American Sociological Review*, 20:5 (October 1955), 531–538; Sam Schulman, "Basic Functional Roles in Nursing: Mother Surrogate and Healer," in E. Gartly Jaco (ed.), *Patients, Physicians, and Illness* (New York: The Free Press, 1958), pp. 528–537; and Miriam M. Johnson and Harry W. Martin, "A Sociological Analysis of the

Nurse Role," *The American Journal of Nursing*, 58:3 (March 1958), 373–377. Their analyses of sex and family roles follow either Sigmund Freud or Talcott Parsons, *Family, Socialization and Interaction Process* (New York: The Free Press, 1955).

61. Parsons, *Family, Socialization and Interaction Process*, especially Ch. 6.

62. A common finding in surveys of public attitudes toward the hospital is that patients depend heavily on nurses for emotional support. E.g., Joachim Israel, "Vad tycker patienterna?" *Tidskrift för sveriges Sjuksköterskor*, 28:22 (November 1961), 856–857; and Ann Cartwright, *Human Relations and Hospital Care* (London: Routledge & Kegan Paul, 1964), Ch. 3.

63. Everett C. Hughes, *Twenty Thousand Nurses Tell Their Story* (Philadelphia: Lippincott, 1958), pp. 50, 211, 214, and probably every other American study; Judith Shuval, *Choosing the Nursing Profession* (Jerusalem: Ministry of Health and Israel Institute of Applied Social Research, 1961); Judith Shuval, "Factors Conditioning Recruitment of Nurses in Israel," *Journal of Health and Human Behavior*, 3:2 (Summer 1962), pp. 82–88; Petersen, "African Nurse Training," p. 329; M. Mury, "Sociologie des élèves infirmières: Compte-rendu de l'enquête" (Sèvres: unpublished paper presented to the Journées d'étude reservées aux monitrices des écoles, 1961), p. 5; Ray E. Trussell et al., *Medical and Hospital Care in Puerto Rico* (New York: School of Public Health and Administrative Medicine, Columbia University, 1962), pp. 156 and 170; Sheila Bevington, *Nursing Life and Discipline* (London: H. K. Lewis, 1943), p. 35; Jillian M. MacGuire, *From Student to Nurse: The Induction Period* (Oxford: Area Nurse Training Committee, 1961), pp. 48–49; Shirley Epir, "Profile of the Turkish Nurse" (New York: Institute of Research and Service in Nursing Education, Teachers College, 1964), pp. 38–40; Pauline Estelle King, "Potential Use of Nurses," Ch. 6, pp. 2–3 and 5–7; H. A. Goddard, *The Work of Nurses in Hospital Wards* (London: The Nuffield Provincial Hospitals Trust, 1954), p. 191; and unpublished Scandinavian surveys.

64. Isabel E. P. Menzies, "A Case-Study of the Functioning of Social Systems as a Defence Against Anxiety," *Human Relations*, 13 (May 1960), 95–121; Thomas S. McPartland, *Formal Education and the Process of Professionalization: A Study of Student Nurses* (Kansas City, Mo.: Community Studies, 1957), pp. 48–54; and Meyer, *Tenderness and Technique*, pp. 91–98.

65. How modern American hospital organization hinders nurses from performing expressive work is described by Chris Argyris, *Diagnosing Human Relations in Organizations: A Case Study of a Hospital* (New Haven: Labor and Management Center, Yale University, 1956); Devereux and Weiner, "Occupational Status of Nurses," and Schulman, "Basic Functional Roles in Nursing."

66. Public opinion surveys elicit few complaints; either patients hesitate to criticize nurses or they no longer expect to receive much emotional support from the hospital staff. Occasionally, popular magazines in the West publish critical articles, such as Samuel Grafton, "Too Busy for Backrubs: Today's Nurse Is an Executive," *McCall's*, September 1959, pp. 52–53; and Dr. X, "Today's Nurse: Is She Sick?" *Show*, May–June 1966, pp. 10–12.

67. Leonard Reissman and John H. Rohrer (eds.), *Change and Dilemma in the*

Nursing Profession (New York: Putnam, 1957), Ch. 3; and Hughes, *Twenty Thousand Nurses*, Ch. 9.

68. For example, an experiment in an American hospital reduced the administrative and housekeeping tasks of staff nurses, so that they would have more time for the bedside care which they said was their principal career motivation. But the nurses felt idle, failed to spend more time with patients and looked for new tasks to keep busy. Peter Kong-Ming New, *Nursing Service and Patient Care* (Kansas City, Mo.: Community Studies, Inc., 1959).

69. This is explained more fully in William A. Glaser, "Nursing Leadership and Policy: Some Cross-National Comparisons," in Fred Davis (ed.), *The Nursing Profession* (New York: Wiley, 1966) pp. 21–22 and 29–30.

70. William Caudill, "Observations on the Cultural Context of Japanese Psychiatry," in Marvin K. Opler (ed.), *Culture and Mental Health* (New York: Macmillan, 1959), pp. 216, 221–222, and 232–236; William Caudill, "Around the Clock Patient Care in Japanese Psychiatric Hospitals: The Role of the Tsukisoi," *American Sociological Review*, 26:2 (April 1961), 204–214; and Edwin L. Crosby, "Observations on Japanese Hospitals," *Hospitals*, 31:15, Part 1 (1 August 1957), 35 and 37.

71. Sheila Bevington, *Nursing Life and Discipline* (London: H. K. Lewis, 1943), pp. 6–7; and *Report of the Working Party on the Recruitment and Training of Nurses* (London: H. M. S. O., 1947), pp. 36 and 45–46.

72. John Hajnal, "The Marriage Boom," in Joseph J. Spengler and Otis D. Duncan (eds.), *Demographic Analysis: Selected Readings* (New York: The Free Press, 1956), pp. 226–227; and Goode, *World Revolution and Family Patterns,* passim.

73. E.g., "Marriage and Nursing," *Nursing Times*, 54:12 (21 March 1958), 337.

74. *Recent Trends in Fertility in Industrialized Countries* (New York: Bureau of Social Affairs, Population Branch, The United Nations, 1958), Ch. 4; Hajnal, "The Marriage Boom"; and Goode, *World Revolution and Family Patterns*, pp. 40–49.

75. C. E. V. Leser, "Trends in Women's Work Participation," *Population Studies*, 12, Part 2 (November 1958), 100–110; Viola Klein, *Women Workers: Working Hours and Services* (Paris: Organisation for Economic Co-Operation and Development, 1965), pp. 18–22.

76. E.g., P. Chombart de Lauwe et al., "Images of Women in Society," *International Social Science Journal*, 14:1 (1962), passim; and Audrey Hunt, *A Survey of Women's Employment* (London: Government Social Survey, 1968), Vol. I, p. 188, and Vol. II, Table K.9.

77. The diffuse quality of women's occupational goals and the compatibility of these goals with domesticity are reported by Ralph H. Turner, "Some Aspects of Women's Ambition," *The American Journal of Sociology*, 70:3 (November 1964), 271–285.

78. Elizabeth Douvan and Carol Kaye, *Adolescent Girls* (Ann Arbor: Institute for Social Research, University of Michigan, 1957), pp. 39–41 and 48–49; Rose K. Goldsen, *What College Students Think* (Princeton: Van Nostrand, 1960), pp. 46–59; and H. Marjorie Simpson, *Accommodation for Nurses and Midwives* (London: The Royal College of Nursing, 1961).

79. E.g., Jean Meyer and Jean-Jacques Gillon, "Pourquoi les infirmières diplomées abandonnent-elles leur profession?" *Le concours médical*, 83:29 (22 July 1961), 4027; "Resultat av lönestatistiken," *Tidskrift för Sveriges Sjuksköterskor,* 18 and 20 (27 September and 27 October 1959); and Rosmarie Lang and Magdelaine Comtesse, *Les services infirmiers en Suisse face aux exigences actuelles et futures* (Berne: La Croix-Rouge Suisse, 1959), pp. 32–35.

80. "Discrimination in Employment or Occupation on the Basis of Marital Status," *International Labour Review*, 85:3 and 4 (March and April 1962), 262–282 and 368–389.

81. E.g., the Swiss figures in Lang and Comtesse, *Les services infirmiers en Suisse,* pp. 32–35.

82. Evelyn B. Moses, "The Profile of a Professional Nurse," *American Journal of Nursing*, 60:3 (March 1960), 368.

83. Simpson, *Accommodation for Nurses and Midwives*, p. 15.

84. In many countries, the single career woman who emulates the Westerner is deviant, may attract gossip and advances from men, may not find housing, and is often pressed by her family to marry. E.g., Margaret Cormack, *The Hindu Woman* (New York: Teachers College, 1953), pp. 167–171.

85. George C. Fetter, "A Comparison between the Christian and Moslem Religions as Factors in Attitudes of Lebanese Farmers" (St. Louis: unpublished paper presented at the American Sociological Association meetings, 1961), p. 6.

86. "Nursing Education in Africa—W.H.O. Conference in Kampala," *International Nursing Review*, 2:1 (April 1955), 15.

87. *Ibid.*, p. 14; Petersen, "African Nurse Training," p. 331; and Woodsmall, *Women and the New East*, p. 170.

88. King, "Potential Use of Nurses," Ch. 3, p. 4, and Ch. 6, pp. 11–15; and Cormack, *The Hindu Woman*, p. 170.

89. E.g., the modernizing changes in the families of African nurses, described in Martin Jarrett-Kerr, *African Pulse: Scenes from an African Hospital Window* (London: The Faith Press, 1960), pp. 100–104.

90. E.g., Hughes, *Twenty Thousand Nurses,* Ch. 5.

91. Hours and weekly schedules for lay graduate nurses in many countries are reported in *Employment and Conditions of Work of Nurses* (Geneva: International Labour Office, 1960), Ch. 4; and *Employment Conditions of Nurses in Selected*

European Countries (London: International Council of Nurses, 1965).

92. E.g., the American staff nurses described in "What Nurses Like and Dislike about Their Jobs," *The Modern Hospital*, 89:6 (December 1957), 54–55.

93. Bethina A. Bennett, "Part-Time Nursing Employment in Great Britain," *International Labour Review*, 85:4 (April 1962), 348.

94. *Part-Time Employment for Women* (Washington: Women's Bureau, U.S. Department of Labor, 1960), p. 29; and Harry W. Martin and Fred E. Katz, "The Professional School as a Molder of Motivations," *The Journal of Health and Human Behavior*, 2 (Summer 1961), 111.

95. Klein, *Women Workers*, pp. 45–51 and 75–77; "Part-Time Employment for Women with Family Responsibilities," *International Labour Review*, 75:6 (June 1957), 545–549; and "An International Survey of Part-Time Employment," *International Labour Review*, 88:4 and 5 (October and November 1963), pp. 380–407 and 490–517.

96. The trend is not occurring without dispute: in several countries, older leaders oppose part-time work on the grounds that it undermines the sense of vocation that is the essence of nursing. E.g., Marlies Cremer, "Probleme der Teilzeitarbeit für Krankenschwestern," *Deutsche Schwesternzeitung*, 16:4 (10 April 1963), 119.

97. Paul C. Glick, *American Families* (New York: Wiley, 1957), pp. 88–94 and 196.

98. Sanford M. Dornbusch and David M. Heer, "The Evaluation of Work by Females, 1940–50," *The American Journal of Sociology*, 63:1 (July 1957), 27–29.

99. Hughes, *Twenty Thousand Nurses*, pp. 258–260; Louise Alcott, "Combining Marriage and Nursing," *American Journal of Nursing*, 55:11 (November 1955), 1344–1346; and Ann C. Hansen, "Can More Nurses Be Recruited?" *New York State Nurse*, 30:4 (May 1958), 10.

100. Frederick R. Wolf, "The Newly Graduated Nurse," *Hospitals*, 32:20 (16 October 1958), 58–62.

101. E.g., Quinton M. Sherrer, "This Nursery Brings Nurses Back to Work," *The Modern Hospital*, 89:6 (December 1957), 59–61.

102. Alva Myrdal and Viola Klein, *Women's Two Roles: Home and Work* (London: Routledge & Kegan Paul, 1956), Chs. 2 and 3; Richard M. Titmuss, *Essays on "The Welfare State"* (London: Allen & Unwin, 1958), Ch. 5; *Demographic Aspects of Manpower: Sex and Age Patterns of Participation in Economic Activities* (New York: Bureau of Social Affairs, Population Branch, The United Nations, 1962), pp. 26–53 passim; and Viola Klein, *Women Workers*, pp. 18–23.

103. Myrdal and Klein, *Women's Two Roles*, pp. 82–87; Viola Klein, *Working Wives* (London: Institute of Personnel Management, 1960), pp. 13–14 and 24–31; Audrey Hunt, *A Survey of Women's Employment* (London: Government Social Survey, 1968), pp. 54–63 and 181; and possibly the middle class respondents in

Murray Gendell, *Swedish Working Wives* (Totowa, N.J.: The Bedminster Press, 1963), pp. 96–98 and 116–120.

104. E.g., Elsie Ensing, "Nursing Auxiliaries—Crawley Hospital," *Nursing Times*, 58:6 (9 February 1962), 159.

105. David R. Mace, "The Employed Mother in the U.S.S.R.," *Marriage and Family Living*, 23:4 (November 1961), 330–333.

106. Myrdal and Klein, *Women's Two Roles*, Ch. 6; National Manpower Council, *Womanpower* (New York: Columbia University Press, 1957), pp. 180–181, 185–188 and 237–244; and Viola Klein, *Employing Married Women* (London: Institute of Personnel Management, 1961), pp. 19–24 and 33–34. Klein's respondents in English management rated wives lower than unmarried women on measures of job commitment.

107. Hughes, *Twenty Thousand Nurses*, pp. 185 and 239–240; Robert P. Bullock, *What Do Nurses Think of Their Profession?* (Columbia: The Ohio State University Research Foundation, 1954), p. 102; Fred Davis and Virginia L. Olesen, "Initiation into a Women's Profession: Identity Problems in the Status Transition of Coed to Student Nurse," *Sociometry*, 26:1 (March 1963), 93; and unpublished data from William A. Glaser and Francis A. McVey, *The Study of Public Health Nursing Field Experience in the Basic Baccalaureate Program* (New York: Cornell University New York Hospital School of Nursing, 1961). Davis' respondents continued to be interested primarily in family life throughout their nursing education, but their commitment to "work and career" was weaker at the end than at the beginning. Fred Davis and Virginia L. Olesen, "The Career Outlook of Professionally Educated Women: The Case of Collegiate Student Nurses," *Psychiatry*, 28:4 (November 1965), 337–340.

108. Meyer F. Nimkoff and Charles M. Grigg, "Values and Marital Adjustment of Nurses," *Social Forces*, 37:1 (October 1958), 67–70.

109. William A. Shee, "Do We Want the Part-Time Nurse?" *Nursing Mirror*, 109:2853 (4 March 1960), 1954–1955; and Gladys McGregor, "The Realities of Staffing," *The American Journal of Nursing*, 62:11 (November 1962), 56–63.

110. Shee, "The Part-Time Nurse?", p. 1955.

111. *Report of the Ministry of Health for the Year Ended 31st December 1960* (London: H. M. S. O., 1961), Part II, p. 141.

112. Ronald G. Corwin, "Role Conception and Mobility Aspiration" (Minneapolis: unpublished dissertation for the Ph.D. in Sociology, University of Minnesota, 1960).

113. Anthony J. Carr, "The Part-Time Nurse's Dilemma," *Nursing Times*, 62:47 (25 November 1966), 1544–1546.

4

Economics and Urbanism

The hospital is not only a system of organizing the realization of humanitarian ideas. It mobilizes technology and people with technical skills. Its organizational forms are borrowed not only from churches but also from the society's common arrangements for performing any work. Its patients suffer, to considerable extent, from illnesses produced by their living standards and from accidents produced by their employment. Whether they can be treated at home depends on their dwellings. Whether they can come to the hospital depends on their proximity. Therefore some of the most important inputs for the hospital come from the economy and depend on the spatial distribution of the population. Among the most powerful sources of cross-national variations in hospital organizations are differences in the economy and related elements of the social structure.

Demand for Hospital Services

The incidence of illness is high and the life expectancy is low in nearly all societies except the most industrialized. Diseases are common because of unbalanced diets, malnutrition, parasites, and infections. Accidents occur often. Difficult childbirths may permanently damage both mother and baby.[1]

As was said in Chapter 2, many societies have supernatural theories about the etiology and cure of all or some diseases. Since people rely on folk doctors who can identify and propitiate the cause, at first they do not call for Western medicine or hospital services. For those conditions with natural causes and cures, the folk doctor and traditional home remedies are used. The folk doctor's support depends on his ability to make quick diagnoses, identify the central cause of the illness, and administer the cure that has quick effects. Particularly since the introduction of antibiotics, hospital outpatient departments and health centers in much of Africa, the Middle East, Asia, and Latin America have been able to offer as spectacular results as any folk doctor, and the news has spread. The effects of penicillin, sulfa drugs, B.C.G., and other Western medicines upon yaws, leprosy, venereal diseases, tuberculosis, and other endemic native diseases have attracted to hospitals and clinics vast numbers of patients who think of the Western-style doctor as a superior kind of folk doctor. So throughout Asia, Africa, the Middle East, and Latin America, one hears of patients incessantly demanding injections—preferably at the location of pain, where folk doctors customarily apply their medications and fetishes. Many patients resist hospitalization after treatment, because they assume that an injection and a short rest at home are sufficient, just as in the regime of folk medicine. Some patients do not understand the function of diagnostic tests, assume that such active procedures must be therapeutically beneficial, and demand blood counts, urinalyses, or stool analyses.[2]

Favorable news increases use of the hospital's ambulatory services. Hearing of the success of injections, more of the population brings that type of condition to the hospital. If certain surgical problems are not deemed of supernatural origin and if they are not taken to the folk doctor, they too are brought to the hospital. Besides the departments for infectious diseases susceptible to antibiotics, orthopedics and the first aid department get larger numbers of outpatients.

When the hospital staff notices the increased utilization, it may try to hold and extend its clientele by giving the patients what they want, even against the staff's own judgment of clinical need and administrative rationality. For example, because patients are very insistent, because doctors are hurried, and because refusals may alienate precarious public opinion, doctors may reluctantly give unnecessary injections.[3] Some Western-style doctors may emulate the methods of folk doctors by making snap diagnoses, appearing to consult the spirit world, and administering treatments theatrically. Often controversies arise within the hospital staff about the best ways to teach the public to use the hospital effectively. Some doctors and nurses favor gradualism: concessions to folk belief are mixed with administration of Western medicine, so that patients' anxieties will be alleviated and the influential folk doctors and prayer leaders will not be antagonized. Other staff members oppose all folk practices, on the grounds that the public can best be educated to learn Western medicine and to use the hospital by seeing the entire system of Western practices as a unit. In South Africa, Jarrett-Kerr believes that white doctors are more favorable to the gradualist method of modernizing the patients' habits, while the African doctors and graduate nurses—who have themselves assimilated much modern thinking and behavior—favor a complete break with customary practices.[4]

Because of the higher disease incidence and the shortage of community health services, the outpatient departments soon become far more crowded in underdeveloped than in developed countries.[5] The indices of modernization do not correlate perfectly, and in particular, urbanization sometimes proceeds faster than literacy and income per capita.[6] In such countries—Egypt, India, South Africa and others—each outpatient department of many urban hospitals gets between 1,500 and 2,200 patients a day, up to ten times the daily load in comparable hospitals in developed countries.

Hospital beds are not always used to the same extent as outpatient departments, and sometimes one finds empty beds at the same time the O.P.D. is overwhelmed. Resistance to hospitalization has various causes. Ambulatory treatment is no different from the customary methods of folk doctors, but what is most novel and worrisome about Western medical care is living away from home in an organization; women may be particularly anxious about living in a hospital run by strangers and men. Men are needed at home if they are the only wage earners. Women may be needed at home to care for children. The high mortality rates of hospitals and rumors about autopsies may frighten people. Doctors or other employees may antagonize local people by treating them inconsiderately. In order to keep their customers, local folk doctors may spread rumors that damage the hospital's reputation.[7]

But, just as in the case of the outpatient departments, the manifest success of inpatient treatment and the modernization of family structure lead to gradual and then rapid increases in hospitalization. The classes, ethnic groups, and religious denominations with the highest literacy, with the greatest geographical mobility, with the most modern family structures, and with the most modern theories of disease—such as the higher classes and the Christians —from the start use outpatient and inpatient services more than others.[8] Eventually utilization becomes very heavy, particularly in the large cities of overpopulated developing countries. For example, in many urban hospitals in India, Pakistan, Egypt, and Indonesia, bed occupancy ranges between 100 percent and 250 percent of listed capacity.

Patients become hospitalized at a later or at a more acute stage of illness in underdeveloped countries. One reason is that the average citizen of an underdeveloped country normally experiences lassitude and symptoms from various chronic conditions, such as malnutrition, birth defects, and parasites, and therefore he is late to recognize the symptoms of a new and dangerous illness. Compared to the citizen of a developed country, he has learned less about symptoms from the mass media and from medical personnel. His continued presence in the family may be indispensable to its precarious economy, until he becomes completely helpless. He may first try certain folk remedies, such as incantations against evil spirits or taking the folk doctor's medicines. Compared to the Westerner, the patient may be much slower in learning the hospital's location and admission procedure. Often patients must take long trips to reach the hospital. Before women and children can go to the hospital, the head of the family (such as the husband, or, in matrilineal societies, someone like the maternal uncle) must give his permission, and he may be travelling far away or may be uninterested.[9] Because of the larger number of acute illnesses brought to hospitals and because so many of the patients were brought in as a result of accidents and other violence, the inpatient population of underdeveloped countries has a larger proportion of surgical cases.

Certain services are much less developed in preindustrial than in modernized countries, because of differences in theories of disease, family structure, and valuation of the patient. One of the most widespread theories of disease in the world is that difficult labor is a punishment for a sin, such as adultery.[10] Therefore cases of complicated childbirth among the rural masses or among the urban proletariat almost never come to the public hospital until after the native midwife and folk doctor have failed. Consequently, public hospitals in many underdeveloped countries get few obstetrical cases, and many of these are advanced emergencies. The usual feedback processes do not expand obstetrical services in hospitals in all countries alike. Even though populations may see that hospital deliveries are successful and even though they steadily increase the use of hospitals for other conditions, national customs produce great differences in rates of obstetrical hospitalization for countries with otherwise comparable economic institutions. In general, more mothers come to the hospital in the more prosperous and more literate societies, but some highly modern countries—notably Holland—still have many home deliveries by midwives, because births are still perceived as normal family functions.[11] However, modernization makes a clear difference in that complicated deliveries are anticipated and hospitalized.

Inpatient hospitalization of children is greater in the more prosperous than in the less wealthy countries, and a consistent cycle exists. In the least developed countries, malnutrition and mortality are high among children, and very few are brought by parents to hospitals. More boys are brought than girls.[12] The public's apathy about the care of children may be shared by the government, which provides few pediatric services.[13] Because the field is unfashionable and there is little teaching material in hospitals, usually few doctors decide to specialize in pediatrics.[14] In a few countries where child care is least developed, the small number of pediatric wards in urban public hospitals are primarily custodial establishments for orphans.

In slightly more developed countries, the situation is quite different. The government may have initiated maternal and child health services and health education programs; mothers are more interested in bringing their children to the clinics and hospitals, because they have heard about the efficacy of care. Because the national birth rates are high, half the public hospital patients in moderately developed countries may be children, and pediatrics suddenly changes from the least important field to one of the busiest.[15]

Among the most modernized and prosperous countries, birth rates are much lower, child health is much better, and thus children represent only a small fraction of all hospital inpatients. The sick child is so exceptional that pediatricians in the highly developed countries now are perplexed by their specialty's future and its place in the hospital.[16]

Recruitment and Allocation of Personnel

Less developed countries generally have shortages of professionally trained persons. Severe social problems are created by poverty, disease, the periodic droughts and economic depression that afflict the rural areas, and the movement of peasants into city slums. The educational system produces too few people to apply expert knowledge to these social problems, and the professionals prefer to live in cities, while the less modernized populations are predominantly rural. Because of shortages of power and equipment, the doctors and other professionals get too little experience in technical procedures during their training, which is predominantly theoretical. These shortages of power and equipment mean that few people grow up with daily experience in technical work, and few technicians are trained.

Doctors. The urban-rural imbalance in the distribution of physicians is more severe in the less affluent than in the developed countries. Following are the numbers of persons per doctor[17] in several countries:

Country	Capital City	Rest of Country
Egypt	700	3,500
Thailand	600	25,000
Tanganyika	1,500	31,000
Philippines	571	5,000
Sweden	450	1,400
France	485	1,100

Although Sweden and France have urban concentrations far more extreme than do other modernized societies, the imbalances in the less industrial countries are far worse.

Discrepancies in staffing are evident in hospitals. Ratios between medical staffs and hospital beds are more unfavorable in the underdeveloped than in the developed countries, particularly in the rural areas. Rural-urban imbalances in doctor-bed and doctor-population ratios exist in developed countries, of course, but they are even greater in underdeveloped countries. For example, the doctor-bed ratio in general hospitals in the northernmost county of Sweden is about 1:17,[18] but in African and Asian towns one often finds 100-bed or larger hospitals with only two or three doctors.[19] Needless to say, doctors in such bush hospitals are extremely overworked because they must perform customary inpatient tasks and often have an enormous outpatient caseload. Usually there are midwives and sometimes a specially trained assistant doctor to carry part of the medical duties.

The urban concentration is greater in the underdeveloped than in the developed countries for various reasons. The small number of rich people are in cities, and therefore a rural hospital doctor cannot supplement his usually low government salary with private practice. Only the biggest urban hospitals are used for specialty training. Small towns are culturally desolate for the doctor and his family. Communication between the capital and rural towns is poor, and a doctor living away from the capital risks losing his influence and professional alliances.

Rapidly developing societies suffer the paradox of medical over-staffing of hospitals in the cities while rural and remote hospitals are drastically understaffed. Economic development affects the country unevenly: the cities become modern, prosperous, and inviting, while the distant villages remain untouched; many city-dwellers are trained, while the peasants remain uncultured. During rapid economic development, the output of doctors exceeds the growth of the public's capacity to pay for private practice. Because these young doctors shrink from the available rural careers, they turn to the urban hospitals. Therefore, in several countries now in the stages of take-off or of maturation—such as Italy, Spain, the Soviet Union, and Turkey—urban hospitals have too many doctors while rural hospitals have hardly any. For example, while parts of

Italy have no or few doctors,[20] some hospitals in Rome have one salaried doctor for every seven to nine beds, plus many young men who work as unpaid volunteers in order to make contacts and build a practice. The numerous Soviet doctors who avoid taking rural polyclinic and rural hospital assignments seem to gravitate to hospitals in Russian cities and provincial capitals,[21] and some of the urban hospital-polyclinic complexes have one doctor for every three to five beds. While eastern Turkish hospitals have few doctors,[22] some of the Ankara and Istanbul hospitals have one doctor to every three beds. In all these countries, one of the service chief's problems is how to keep his medical staff busy.

The higher the level of economic development of a country, then the more advanced its medical technique, the more skilled and varied its equipment and chemical industries, the larger the number of technicians trained for hospital employment, and therefore the greater the number and complexity of equipment and laboratories in that country's hospitals. The multiplication and increasing complexity of equipment and laboratories in a country's hospitals make their organizations larger and more complex. New medical specialties arise, so there is a greater division of labor and greater heterogeneity within the medical staff. The visitor to a typical hospital in an underdeveloped country meets only general surgeons and internists in the surgical and medical fields. Such countries have only a few subspecialists in the surgical and medical areas, and they are concentrated in the few teaching hospitals; in some new technical specialties, there may be no licentiate. Table 1 compares the numbers of fully licensed specialists in the entire medical profession in certain fields in a few developed and underdeveloped countries.[23]

Therefore hospitals in less developed countries have less differentiated medical staffs and simpler departmental structures. Fewer communications and coordination tasks beset the director.

Technicians. An even greater contrast between the more modernized and less affluent countries appears in the number and specialized categories of trained technicians. For example, in 1960 the English and Welsh hospitals in the National Health Service employed 2,729 "medical laboratory technicians" and were training 2,587 students.[24] At the same time in Turkey, public hospital

TABLE 1

	United States (1963)	Sweden (1963)	Thailand (1962)	Iran (1964)	Ghana (1962)
Internal medicine	37,429	1,026	25	40	18
Cardiology	1,703	323	5	17	3
Gastroenterology	561	82	3	11	2
Allergy	831	0	1	0	1
General surgery	25,331	565	25	344	20
Neurosurgery	1,817	15	4	1	0
Thoracic surgery	1,291	0	10	0	0
Plastic surgery	990	13	6	6	0
Total number of licensed doctors	272,502	7,940	3,588	7,090	595
Total number of licensed specialists	176,573	3,023	260	1,511	120

laboratories are listed as employing 38 diplomaed laboratory technicians, 38 "workers," and 76 "servants."[25] On the basis of 2,729 English laboratory technicians, 38 Turkish technicians, and the hospital bed totals reported by the World Health Organization,[26] the technician-bed ratios are 1:177 for England and 1:1,180 for Turkey. Less developed countries have even fewer trained technicians than Turkey.[27] Certain specialized technicians found in hospitals in developed countries—English hospital staffs include such people as "electroencephalography recordists," "occupational therapists," "darkroom technicians," "remedial gymnasts,"[28]—do not exist in Turkey or in less developed countries. (England is a big country with many beds, but even small developed countries have a larger number and variety of technicians than does Turkey.)[29]

Nurses. Since professional education for nurses is recent in all underdeveloped countries, the shortage of graduate nurses is much greater than in developed countries.[30] The nurse-bed difference is very large when comparing remote parts of the two classes of countries. For example, in the northern county of Sweden the ratio of graduate nurses to beds is about 1:5.[31] But in some of the cities of Eastern Turkey, hospitals of up to 350 beds have five or fewer professionally trained nurses apiece, and some cities have no graduate nurses at all.[32] Most hospitals in Latin Americe lack even one graduate nurse.[33] The nursing care is given by a few practical nurses with brief training and by many untrained auxiliaries.

The shortage of graduate nurses is qualitative as well as quantitative, since the graduate nurse may have gotten much less education than in modernized countries. For example, in Egypt until recently, the graduate nurse (called a *hakima*) officially entered nursing school at the age of sixteen (often fourteen, in practice) after graduating from the five-year primary school. She would then study nursing and midwifery for five years. Except for the English matrons and ward sisters, the *hakimas* were the elite of Egyptian nursing and were among the few educated Egyptian women. For many years only about fourteen *hakimas* were graduated annually, and a count in 1961 showed there were only 368 for 7,805 beds in the principal public hospitals of Egypt; 1,281 auxiliaries trained in one-year apprenticeship courses, students, and other untrained employees were doing most of the work in the wards.[34] The Nasser government has tried to improve the education of *hakimas* and develop collegiate nursing schools that can attract intelligent girls who presently prefer schoolteaching and medicine.

Lower ranks. Underdeveloped countries usually have large numbers of unskilled, poorly nourished, and inefficient persons who are unemployed or partially employed. A visitor to a hospital in an underdeveloped country soon notices many such persons about. They clean, carry messages, stand at doors, help lift things, and wait for any assignment that a professional or administrator can devise.[35] Partly their presence is due to local customs of overstaffing every organization at the unskilled low-paid ranks; sometimes governments or religious missions who own these hospitals are intentionally providing work relief for the local unemployed men. Administrative studies of other organizations in underdeveloped countries also show such imbalanced staffing, with shortages of the skilled and surpluses of the unskilled.[36]

While servants, cleaners, and housekeepers are a minority of the hospital employees in most developed countries, often they are a majority in hospitals in underdeveloped countries. Their exact numbers are impossible to estimate, because such hospitals usually do not keep records about them. Hardie counted the 1,000 hospital employees of Bahrain and estimates 40 doctors, 170 graduate nurses, 130 nursing auxiliaries, and 485 domestics, watchmen, messengers, sweepers, cleaners, etc.[37] A 56-bed rural hospital in northern Brazil is reported to have 4 doctors, 3 nurses, 26 auxiliaries and 55 "others."[38] I visited a 1,350-bed Turkish hospital that had 481 doctors, 162 nurses and nursing auxiliaries, 22 office workers, and about 730 maintenance workers—among whom paramedical personnel were a small minority.

The large number of idling unskilled persons in such hospitals, particularly in the tropics, makes the work tempo and general atmosphere much slower than in Western hospitals. Certainly an organization with a homogeneous mass of interchangeable unskilled employees strikes the visitor differently than a more modernized hospital, where nearly everyone is a somewhat unique individual rapidly performing some specialized technical task.

Goals and Performance

Despite the great differences in staffing and social setting, hospital doctors in less industrialized and less urbanized countries attempt the same sort of work as their teachers and counterparts in the West. In other words, they use scientific knowledge to diagnose and treat the physical problems presented to them by individual patients. This conception of the hospital fits into the social systems of modernized countries: these societies are stable and prosperous, deviant behavior is exceptional, the average patient has no more than a few conditions, his maladies are curable and often self-limiting, and the patient can easily reoccupy satisfying economic and family statuses.[39]

Doctors in preindustrial countries are eager to perform the traditional therapist role for numerous reasons. This is the image of medical practice created by the West and confirmed by the folk doctor's traditional roles. To become an educated Western-style doctor is one of the most respected statuses in underdeveloped countries, just as in the modernized societies themselves.[40] Perhaps the respect for medicine is even stronger in underdeveloped countries, since in many, it has long been one of the few avenues by which status-conscious citizens could get an education and could enter the Western-oriented elite.[41] Having entered a medical career, the doctor's preference for clinical therapy is reinforced by many forces: the indigenous doctor who studies in Europe or America learns the clinical roles designed for developed societies; the doctor who studies in his home country attends a school whose curriculum is copied from Europe and whose faculty includes many therapy-minded Europeans; after graduation he soon learns that he can become rich and powerful in his own country best by duplicating the successful European combination of urban private practice and ownership of a private clinic. So, in many underdeveloped countries, particularly those with shortages of doctors, physicians try to avoid full-time salaried government employment in public health or in other fields, and they try to become private therapists catering to the small elite of government officials and businessmen on a fee-for-service basis.[42] When they work in the public hospital —either during their graduate training or in part-time jobs thereafter—doctors in less developed countries try to play the same clinical roles that are common in hospitals in more modernized societies.

Patient roles. If an organization achieves its original goals, all parts of its own social system must operate as expected, and it must obtain the right combination of inputs. The hospital can successfully treat individual patients in the modernized societies, but many of the prerequisites are absent in preindustrial societies.

The clinical performance of the hospital depends on a set of social relations with the patient. The sick person is not merely a client but must become a participant in an organization with a definite set of roles. In the hospital organizations existing in modernized countries and emulated by the less industrialized societies, the patient roles involve temporary suspension from one's normal statuses, active cooperation with the hospital staff, and steady progress toward discharge and full resumption of normal occupational and family roles outside.[43] This presupposes a total social system in which all persons are fully employed in satisfying occupational and family statuses, all persons have acquired the intellectual ability to understand the hospital's expectations, patients are not too socially distant from the doctors and nurses, the status of professional is understood and trusted, and people customarily struggle to achieve their goals. Further, this model assumes diseases capable of rapid cycles of affliction and recovery.

For the great mass of patients in preindustrial countries, certain specific presuppositions of the modernized hospital inpatient roles are particularly troublesome. One is intellectual understanding. Most persons never have learned the anatomical, physiological, and chemical abstractions necessary for the doctor's explanation and health teaching. Even their language may be prescientific.[44] For example, an Arab doctor told me:

> Arabic lacks all the modern medical ideas in its vocabulary. That is a serious obstacle to health education and public health. When I have a patient here in my office and try to explain what he should do, he cannot understand half of it. There are no words for medical things in Arabic. You and I can sit here and discuss things in English and understand. In our conversation this evening, we understood words like "penicillin," "gastrectomy," and so on. But I cannot do that with an Arabic-speaking patient.

Other elements in the communication relationship may be impaired, too. A patient cannot report fully or accurately to a doctor if he does not know the meaning of chronological age, if he cannot relate different events in a time sequence in order to describe the evolution of symptoms, and if he thinks that all illnesses are the sudden results of bewitchment.[45] Even though doctor and patient in modernized societies may belong to different social classes, communication and trust are not blocked by membership in altogether different social milieux. But many underdeveloped countries have deep internal divisions, and the average patient is confused by the fact that he is communicating with a member of the powerful, Westernized, and urban elite. The patient may rarely have conversed with such a person before and is not accustomed to a relationship in which an elite person asks him about himself. The doctor in turn may be rude. As a long-established member of village society, of course, the folk doctor can be consulted by the patient with less difficulty.[46]

The dependency component in the Western patient role is another subtle element that eludes many patients in underdeveloped countries. The patient is supposed to be completely dependent on the doctor so long as the latter sees a medical need, and to be completely independent thereafter. But an undercurrent of voluntarism, rational choice, and activism characterizes the patient. Although dependent on the doctor's superior medical knowledge, he is not totally dependent on the doctor as a person or as a magical representative of the gods. Doctors are assumed to be fallible, and the patient remains a free and autonomous person; so, the patient supposedly selects the doctor by rational act, withdraws if he suspects malpractice, and participates actively in his own recovery through questioning and striving. But all this presupposes a social system that has certain properties: patients understand and trust doctors and scientific medicine; physicians are conscientious and disinterested; the patient's family and economic roles motivate him both to be cured completely by scientific standards and to resume his normal life as soon as he can with safety.

The subtle nature of dependence on a completely secular doctor is difficult to understand in many preindustrial societies. Many people are accustomed to visiting a magical folk doctor and being totally and uncritically dependent on him; complete dependence on gods is a familiar religious response, and the folk doctor often is acting as a semi-divine mediator. Instead of the Western-style calculated and freely chosen dependence on a scientific doctor, patients in underdeveloped countries may try to be as totally dependent, unquestioning, and passive with him as with any witch doctor; when he refuses to be omniscient, behaves as a partner in an active relationship, and asks questions, such patients may be disturbed and alienated.

On the other hand, some patients in underdeveloped countries deviate from the optimum dependency relation in the other direction. Since the doctor is a man and not a magician, he may not be trusted enough; because Western scientific medicine is made by men and not by spirits, it may not be respected enough.[47] Defiance of medical judgment by premature departure from the hospital is a widespread problem in several preindustrial countries where the hospital seems unnatural to the patient and where family obligations continually tug at him. Such patients may not understand the difference between alleviation of symptoms and a full cure, and they assume that illnesses come suddenly and can be sent away suddenly by the methods either of witch doctors or of scientific doctors. A serious public health menace in some underdeveloped countries today is the sudden departure of tuberculosis patients from the hospital as soon as their symptoms disappear.[48] In some countries with many beggars, such people may be motivated to enter the hospital, but they resist cures, since deformities are essential to their occupation.[49] Public understanding and cooperation with hospitals require high rates of recovery which are threatened by premature discharge.

The modern hospital presupposes the right balance between dependence on the doctor and dependence on groups outside the hospital. But when a society develops faith in doctors, it may lack other conditions motivating discharge when medically feasible. In particular, in modernizing countries with high unemployment and no job security during illnesses, many patients may prefer the security of hospital life to the risks of the labor market. Some hospitals in Latin America, the less industrialized countries of Europe, and parts of Asia encounter substantial resistance to discharge.

Following doctors' orders after discharge is essential to the modern hospital inpatient role but also is troublesome in many underdeveloped countries. Advising a patient about changes in diet and sanitation presupposes his ability to perceive how one action in the present—an often unpleasant or inconvenient action—will produce a future result that is apparently unconnected with the precipitating action. Such futuristic thinking, self-denial, and comprehension of chains of events are much less common in preindustrial countries. It is easy for a patient to go to a clinic and ask the scientific doctor, like the folk doctor, to employ his magic for an instantaneous cure; but to modify the behavior and thinking learned from one's forefathers is a different matter.[50] Thus, a chronic frustration of Egyptian hospital doctors is that they cure patients of bilharziasis, warn them not to walk in canals, and know that the patients will re-enter the canals and will become reinfected. Similarly, many an African mother has agreed to make simple changes of diet that would eliminate her children's kwashiorkor and then resumes serving the customary protein-deficient foods as soon as she goes home. For these and other reasons, hospitals cannot rely on self-care and family home care. For example, diabetics are taught to take care of themselves in developed countries but may be treated on daily visits to outpatient clinics in some under-developed countries.[51]

Work tempo. The patient composition and late referral have certain effects on the medical and nursing work. Doctors in the hospitals of underdeveloped countries see many medical conditions that long ago disappeared from the medical practice of modernized countries. Visitors often remark at the number and severity of conditions encountered in an ordinary work day.[52] The patient population helps the hospital achieve one of its goals, namely the education of young doctors and nurses. They see unusual cases that Westerners find only in textbooks.[53]

But the overcrowding and emergency tempo in the wards and outpatient departments hamper patient care. Doctors and nurses lack enough time for thorough investigations and for prolonged treatments.[54] Even medical education suffers. Medical school professors in preindustrial countries often complain they lack the space and time required for good teaching rounds. Late referral of patients causes students to see fewer medical conditions in early stages.

The deteriorated conditions of so many patients in the public hospitals in preindustrial and developing countries limits doctors' success: patient stays are longer[55] and fewer patients recover. This is one of the reasons for the doctors' avoidance of the public hospitals in favor of private practice: because the more affluent minorities have higher living standards and seek medical care earlier, they can be cured more often. Therapeutic success does not climb steadily as countries become more modernized and more prosperous; instead, the problem arises again among the most advanced. When the population is so healthy and so capable of responding to ambulatory treatment that fewer young adults are hospitalized, its life expectancy lengthens. Therefore many modernized countries in recent decades have experienced rapid increases of chronically aged patients. Unless nursing homes are created in large numbers, entire services in public hospitals—such as the wards in internal medicine and cardiology—become custodial rather than therapeutic establishments, to the distress of the doctors and administrators.

Performance of nurses and auxiliaries. The therapeutic success of a hospital depends heavily on the staff of graduate nurses, practical nurses, and nursing auxiliaries. Great differences in hospital organization exist between modernized and preindustrial countries because of the skills of these employees. The less developed a country, the lower the average level of education and the greater the number of people reared in tribal or village homes. Therefore, in the hospital, the fewer the graduate nurses and the lower the education and intellectual skills of the practical nurses and auxiliaries who actually care for the patients. Intellectual differences between doctor and nursing staff consequently are greater in underdeveloped than in developed countries. This is but a concrete example of the belief by many educators and administrators that differentials in ability seem wider in underdeveloped than in advanced countries: in technical and rational work, the ablest people in all societies are equals, but ability drops off more sharply in the less modernized countries.[56]

To work effectively in a modern Westernized hospital, one must have many specific medical skills and appropriate general habits of mind. Learning such skills in a nursing school or as an apprentice in a hospital may be very difficult, particularly if the girl is one of the many persons who has recently entered the city from the tribal areas and villages. Learning such skills is a common problem throughout the labor force in the most underdeveloped countries, such as tropical Africa. Memorization, recitation, and rote performance of acts are admired in many tribal cultures,[57] the preindustrial urban intelligentsia may have developed traditions of rote memorization in school,[58] and the student nurse may approach nursing knowledge and procedures in the same spirit. Many nursing educators are astounded at African students' capacity to memorize and recite facts and to perform complicated procedures in a rehearsed manner, but they are often distressed to discover that the students and practicing nurses may not comprehend the explanations for the facts, may not be curious about reasons and consequences, and may not realize the need to adapt ritualized procedures according to circumstance. Empirical and scientific "explanations" comprehensible to every person (including *women)* may be a culturally unfamiliar idea; facts may customarily be taken for granted in many such cultures, and curiosity about reasons may be rare because of customary referral of puzzles to designated specialists with pat answers, such as priests or other custodians of traditional lore and magic.

Other adjustment and learning problems are encountered by the student nurse, practicing nurse, and auxiliary because of the discontinuities some encounter between village or slum upbringing on the one hand and the nursing school and hospital on the other hand. The hospital requires manual dexterity and familiarity with machines and gadgets; but such experiences may have been absent before, and instead the employee may have acquired typical tribal skills that are not always transferable to the hospital, such as dancing, singing, and reciting folklore and family trees. Many underdeveloped countries are multilingual, and many students, nurses, and auxiliaries must learn and work in a foreign language. Many employees may never have learned the self-reliance required for performance of some hospital tasks.[59]

A widespread problem is violation of sterile technique. Sterilizing equipment at the right time in the right way may be forgotten easily, because the employee never understood the reasons or because he has memorized the procedure by rote and cannot apply it to an unforeseen new situation. Bandages, solutions, or equipment may be contaminated carelessly by someone among the large number of employees in the network handling a sterile supply, because he had never learned or believed the elusive Western ideas about germs and therefore never knew that an apparently innocuous act like touching an object could affect the health of a patient. An employee giving several injections may forget to change the needle; or he may sterilize it, not according to the hospital's procedure, but according to folk beliefs, such as holding the needle over a flame. Since standards of cleanliness in ordinary life are lower than in developed countries, hospital wards are dirtier in underdeveloped countries, particularly on visitors' day.[60] The same differences in asepsis and cleanliness existed between the more and less developed parts of Europe itself at the turn of the century.[61]

As a result of the lower standards of sterile technique and cleanliness, hospital wards in many underdeveloped countries usually have a higher rate of postoperative infection than in the West. For example, in the United States a postoperative infection rate of over 1 percent would arouse a special investigation,[62] but the chief surgeon in the large teaching hospital of one of the preindustrial countries I visited told me that 50 percent of all his patients regularly suffer infections in clean surgical wounds after returning to the wards. Certain medical specialties requiring exceptional sterile technique on the wards, such as plastic surgery, can grow only in the modernized countries. Epidemics of serum hepatitis regularly break out on wards because of injections with unsterile needles. Epidemics of bacillary dysentery may be a recurring hazard in pediatrics.

Medication errors sometimes are made by practical nurses or auxiliaries who lack knowledge, fail to understand, and forget. Wrong medicines may be given, or the dosage may be calculated incorrectly. Numerous modern medicines must be given at specific intervals, but timing errors are common; the practical nurse or auxiliary usually has no watch, the ward may lack a clock, and such employees—like their countrymen—lack the intense time-consciousness so typical of Western hospital personnel.[63] Errors in diagnostic information and in patients' histories also may exist, if practical nurses and auxiliaries cannot read thermometers, take pulses, or fill out records accurately. Since the ward sister's reviews and controls over her staff's performance may be haphazard, many mistakes are never detected. Some underdeveloped countries have great trouble training enough instrument nurses; in this crucial job, one must be rapid, understand the course of the operation, anticipate the surgeon's next needs, and never break asepsis.

The great discrepancy in skill between doctors and ward personnel often produces serious tensions within the hospital organizations in some countries. Convinced that their work is undone by their subordinates, doctors are often visibly angry and contemptuous. Sometimes there is conflict between departments: in one of the Middle Eastern hospitals I visited, recurring cycles of postoperative infection regularly aroused recriminations between the operating room and the ward, mollified on one occasion only because an investigation showed they could join together in blaming the supply room.

Methods of controlling hospital employees sometimes boomerang by inducing them to make medically inaccurate reports to their superiors. For example, in one of the Middle Eastern countries, many hospital administrators try to combat the inefficiency and laxity of hospital employees by levying fines for all infractions. The results can easily be predicted; a clinical nursing instructor told me of one typical result:

> One of my students noticed that all the charts on one ward had similar TPR (temperature, pulse, and respiration) readings. She watched the nurse take TPRs on her rounds, the student then took the same TPRs herself, and she noticed great discrepancies. There were differences between patients. The nurse had to take so many in a short time that she was dishonest, in order to get it done. Also perhaps she did not know how to read a thermometer, how to read a pulse, particularly since most of these nurses lack watches with second hands. Often they tended to mark down a normal temperature for everyone. If I had to take a hundred temperatures between 7 and 7:30 P.M., and if I lost 10 percent of my salary for not doing it, I would cheat too.

In some less developed societies, telling the truth is less valued than maintaining interpersonal harmony. But accurate reporting is indispensable to the hospital. The employee may fear that the truth will arouse punishments from doctors and administrators, who may be hostile upper class natives or frightening Europeans. So in some underdeveloped countries accurate reporting and the detection and correction of errors are chronic problems.

> The tribal definition of truth taught to the young differs from our European version. One may appreciate its basis, yet still realize that somehow nurses must accept our definition, if they are to move into our society professionally. [According to Zulu culture] it would be very rude for a Zulu nurse who had hurt a superior by breaking a thermometer, by allowing a sterilizer to burn dry and ruin its elements, to then admit that she had done it. It would be as though one, very unimportant and weak, boasted of her power to hurt an important and powerful person. She must profess ignorance, deny responsibility for the damage done.[64]

Besides technical and administrative work, nursing also consists of humane personal service and perception of the needs of patients. Western nursing consultants, particularly those who are Christians or have been trained in the patient-oriented and universalistic English tradition, are often surprised to find much weaker attitudes among nurses and auxiliaries in many underdeveloped countries. One reason is that so many hospital employees are from social classes wherein disease, suffering, and death are commonplace. In some cultures the sick person is not considered deserving of special help, but he is considered inferior and worthless until he resumes his normal roles. In many societies the idea of universal service to strangers is inconceivable; one helps fellow clansmen, one may be polite to fellow villagers, but members of another tribe are to be distrusted and certainly not helped.[65] Even though nurses may have entered this career from humanitarian motives and may gain satisfaction from helping the sick, on the other hand they are the products of their society: consequently sometimes they may be indifferent and cross toward demanding patients. If their culture prizes stoicism or warns that surrendering to illness results in losing control of oneself to the witches or demons that sent the illness, the nurses may be cold toward patients in pain.[66] The director of a Christian mission hospital in Natal recalled:

> I have known a few instances in which African nurses appeared callous. For example, unable to sleep one night, I listened to the loud moaning of a patient a hundred feet away on a balcony. Surely the African night nurse at her desk some thirty feet away from her patient would have heard and given a P.R.N. injection of morphine that I had ordered. At last, sleepless and angry, I went across. "Why haven't you given that poor woman her morphine, nurse? Didn't you hear her crying?" "No doctor, I didn't. Has she been crying?" As I lay awake a little later, I wondered how long I could listen to the moaning of a friend or relation in a Zulu home, knowing full well that there was neither doctor, nurse or chemist to give the patient relief from pain. I could easily imagine how soon I would close my ears to the moans that I might be powerless to silence.[67]

One of the motivations for the new collegiate nursing schools in Egypt and Turkey is to recruit upper class girls who might be less inured and callous toward suffering.

Another presupposition of the modern hospital is that everyone will react urgently and rapidly to emergencies. But in many underdeveloped countries, health personnel prefer their countrymen's more leisurely work pace, even in the face of medical situations that a Westerner might think merit an urgent response.[68] The very rapid walking pace, which is an occupational trademark of nurses in developed countries, may be thought a sign of mental derangement.[69]

Finally, the modern Western hospital presumes a high inter-
dependence among its employees. But, the division of labor outside
the family in many preindustrial cities lacks integration and has
little synchronization of effort: each individual tries to be an entre-
preneur, seeking supplies and customers by himself.[70] Insufficient
experience in teamwork is evident in hospital wards. Several of my
informants said they had difficulty inspiring in their ward personnel habits of mutual help without continuous supervision. Some
said that, although ward sisters could learn their scientific and
clerical duties well enough, the ability to be a good supervisor and
team leader came more slowly. If men are accustomed to treating
women only as subordinates, male nurses may not collaborate with
female nurses and may resist the authority of female superiors. A
further complication in Africa is that hospital employees may be
reluctant to work with others from different tribes.[71]

Equipment. Because medicine is the application of machinery and
chemicals, the wealthier and more industrialized countries have the
largest amounts of new equipment. They do not always have the
newest buildlngs. The resources of a country become inputs into
hospitals only as a result of government decisions. Some Western
governments have given priority to staffing, drugs, and equipment
for an expanding number of patients, other sectors of society compete for tax revenues, and the replacement of old buildings is
postponed. Several highly modernized countries—Great Britain,
France, Belgium, and northern Italy—try to conduct modern hospital care in older buildings that are not arranged well for modern
equipment, for numerous technical departments, and for the flow
of patients and communications among departments.[72]

Even when an important piece of equipment is acquired by a less
affluent country, it often cannot be used and incorporated into the
hospital organization because the society lacks the essential infrastructure of suppliers and schools. Because the equipment is usually manufactured in Europe or America for Western hospitals, it
often cannot be operated in an underdeveloped country with unreliable electric current, unreliable water supplies, and high humid-
ity. Equipment and laboratories require technicians, and the
educational system may produce too few.[73] Damage is common
because of inept use and lack of foresight. Busy technical depart-

ments and laboratories require a steady flow of supplies through several pipelines, many underdeveloped countries lack domestic suppliers and efficient supply flows, bottlenecks exist in purchasing and shipment, and shutdowns of service sometimes (or often) occur in the hospital laboratories because of shortages of essential items.[74] One of the common problems throughout developing societies is the shortage of maintenance men and parts, because skilled personnel and materials are too few for both new construction and repair, and modern equipment in the hospitals is often idle until a repair man can be found or until a spare part is imported from the foreign manufacturer.[75] Because underdeveloped countries usually have limited tax resources, medical services are often underfinanced and hospitals cannot maintain stockpiles of drugs and parts that would allow their technical departments to keep working without interruption.[76]

Styles of medical care differ in the hospitals of less developed countries, because of these shortages of equipment and of technically trained persons. The quality of surgery may be seriously handicapped by shortages of anesthesiologists. For example, thoracic surgery requires sophisticated anesthetic techniques and is impossible if no one can run the equipment. In one of the more important tuberculosis hospitals of the Middle East, thoracic surgery can be performed only one morning a week, since an anesthesiologist can be obtained only then and since the doctors do not trust the nurses to be anesthetists for such surgery. Thus many patients requiring surgery cannot be treated. Teaching hospitals may have to use surgical residents or occasional nurses as anesthetists in order to keep the operating room busy, but mistakes and fatal accidents result. A professor of surgery in the Eastern Mediterranean told me that his operating room had lost seven patients on the table the previous year because of heart stoppage.

Technical aids are indispensable to diagnosis in the modern hospital. But if a country has no pathologist or bacteriologist and if a hospital lacks the pathology and bacteriological laboratories necessary for tissue examinations and antibody studies, then hospital doctors may develop skills in visual diagnosis or may acquire the habit of snap diagnosis by symptom.[77] Further limitations may arise from the lack of radiologists and from the erratic operation of X-ray equipment, resulting in unreliable diagnostic X-rays.[78]

If a country's economic institutions can supply hospitals with enough equipment and supplies, they should be available when needed. This requires a respect for public property left in the open. But a common problem in preindustrial and developing countries is the poverty of the hospital's lower employees. A struggle for subsistence is common, and the individual's loyalty to his family usually has priority over his duty to the community. Conceptions of the public interest develop usually only after modernization of the entire society.

As one might expect, probably every hospital in every underdeveloped country suffers a steady theft of food. Many experience regular pilferage of drugs, linen, and equipment, which are then sold in the black market or openly by street vendors.[79] Therefore in most of the hospitals in underdeveloped countries, the graduate nurses lock up much of the hospital's drugs, linen, and equipment.

Modern organizations presuppose the good faith of all employees, so that scrutiny and controls are unnecessary.[80] Preventive measures against thefts often have drastic effects upon the organization and performance of the hospital. For example, in one country I visited, active grapevines of smugglers were suspected among the lower employees of many hospitals, and thefts were very frequent. As a control over personnel, the government and hospital managers designated a certain individual who would be financially responsible for the breakage or disappearance of each piece of equipment. Since replacement of such equipment would be a big deduction from his limited income, each person often tried to keep "his" items locked up at all times, regardless of how this hampered the hospital's work. Disappearance of any piece of equipment would arouse severe tensions in the ward, with the responsible person suspecting certain of the others, while all the others vociferously protested their ignorance of the object's whereabouts.

Effects of staff quality on hospital organization. Some chiefs of service in less developed countries respond fatalistically to the low performance of the public hospital's nursing, technical, and housekeeping personnel. Their private office practices and work in their private clinics have priority in both attention and time, thereby increasing further the atmosphere of pessimism and cynicism surrounding the public hospital.

Some chiefs of service attempt to improve performance, but their remedies have distinctive effects on the structure of the hospital. Because the hospital's central services are not easily observed and controlled, the chief of each clinical service hires his own staff, thereby decentralizing the hospital and creating duplicate structures. The country's shortages of money, equipment, nurses, and technicians are aggravated when each chief tries to create and staff his own operating theater and laboratories. If the doctor uses the hospital's equipment, he may still employ his own staff: for example, a surgeon may have his own surgical team for all his work in either the public hospital or the private clinic.

Another remedy that affects hospital structure is centralization within the work group. The chief of service and his head nurse will perform all life-and-death tasks themselves, delegate few discretionary tasks, and review the performance of subordinates carefully. For example, instead of relying on X-ray technicians, the chief may interpret all X-ray pictures himself and may take many himself. The head nurse may give all injections and intravenous infusions. As a result, the doctor performs more work on each patient, the hospital's productivity is lower than in developed countries, and patient stays are longer. The hospital cannot develop a hierarchy graded by skill, with delegations from higher to lower ranks.[81]

Hospitals in the most modernized countries have staffs capable of reliable performance, and therefore the possibility of delegating responsible work produces a different organization. Duplicating structures are replaced by central services. Power and decision-making no longer are concentrated at the top. The doctor is less omniscient. The physician relies more on laboratory results and other scientific tools, and many physicians concede the uncertainties and cautions that are inherent in modern scientific culture.[82] The multiplication of medical specialists necessitates more interspecialty collaboration, and the increased use of equipment causes the doctor to depend on and collaborate with technicians and administrators in team efforts.[83] An English matron told me about the changes she has observed during her career:

In the old days, the doctor was the leader, not just a member of a group along with nurses. When I was a nurse in training, the doctor was not only the leader of the medical team, but the person whose skill decided whether the patient would live or die. Now there is a medical team that is very large, and other people are important. Take a patient with a stroke; at different stages of his treatment, different people are important. In one stage of the treatment, it is the physiotherapist who is the one who is most important, since he will be the one whose skills will determine whether the patient can walk or use his arm. Doctors now are more dependent on other people, relations are more interdependent than before. The idea of the consultant as a white chief with his followers around him going through the wards has ended. In the old days the nurse opened the door for him, held his towel for him, called him "Sir," looked up to him worshipfully for his orders. But all this has ended. Sometimes even when he is acting as a doctor, he is not the most important factor, but the machine he is working with is more skilled and more important than he is.

The modernization of the hospital. Discrepancies exist between the goals of the hospital and its inputs and organization even in the most affluent and most industrialized societies. The goals of complete and successful care for the public are never reached: as hospitals are improved, the goals are raised both by their staffs and by the public.[84] Therefore, hospitals in all countries experience continuous criticism, reorganization, and expansion. Probably few classes of organizations undergo so much negative feedback, and almost all hospital managements encounter it in every country.

Hospitals in preindustrial and developing countries are particularly beset by internal maladjustments, as this chapter has indicated. The goals of therapy for all inpatients are set by doctors, graduate nurses, and administrators in the light of models in more industrialized and richer countries. But severe barriers exist because of shortages of personnel and equipment, the number and severity of illnesses, the behavior of patients and staff, and the undesired effects of remedial controls and procedures.

One possible response by the staff is flight. Prolonged failure to achieve goals results in increasing difficulties in the retention and recruitment of personnel. Therefore, public hospitals in many underdeveloped countries have persistent shortages of doctors and nurses. The doctors enter private practice or emigrate to richer countries whose hospitals offer higher pay and better facilities.[85]

Women enter careers other than nursing.

However, governments and hospital administrators in developing countries have attempted to alter the inputs of resources and personnel, in order to bring hospitals more into line with those in the richest and most industrialized countries. More money is sought from the government in order to raise the salaries of doctors and nurses. Some countries like Egypt have attempted to transform recruitment into medicine: more sons of workers and farmers are admitted into medical school, in the hope they will be more disposed toward salaried jobs treating the public in hospitals. Several less developed countries—Egypt, Turkey, Colombia, Brazil, the Philippines, and others—have introduced nursing schools into the universities, in the hope that an able, unselfish, and humanitarian nursing leadership will be created. Education for women generally is encouraged, and they are urged to enter nursing and laboratory work.

Improvements are sought in the internal organization of the hospitals in less developed countries. Consultants are invited from the World Health Organization, from European and American technical assistance programs, and from American and British foundations.[86] The rudimentary records and reporting channels are improved. Some hospitals have been connected with local health centers, designed to take the load off the outpatient department.

A serious problem for the hospital in less developed countries has been the patient, and improvement is difficult. More patients learn to come to hospitals. But high birth rates and poverty have continued unabated, and hospitals remain crowded with immense numbers of persons handicapped by poor prognoses, low medical sophistication, and home conditions detrimental to recovery. Really fundamental improvements in the conditions that distress doctors and nurses require transformation in the society at large. Some consultants have urged drastic changes in the priorities in medical planning with far more investment in preventive medicine. Then the hospitals would not be so burdened. But no government has yet abandoned the usual emphasis on therapy of individual patients to such a drastic extent.[87]

Besides reducing the number of severe and chronic diseases, hospitals can function better only if the population is capable of understanding its own medical needs, coming at the right time, communicating with the staff intelligently, and following medical orders. Most developing countries have lacked the mass media, the network of grassroots organizers, and the determination of the government necessary to educate the entire population in the proper methods of playing the role of patient. The Soviet Union may be the only developing country that has succeeded in a short time, to the great benefit of the country's hospitals.[88]

Modernizing Effects of the Hospital

Gradually the hospital is modernized, as the development of a society alters the flow of inputs and as the hospital's management brings the organization closer to the models in the most advanced countries. But because workers and clients participate in the organization, reciprocal effects occur: as the hospital changes, it helps to modernize other social institutions.[89]

Patients. During visits to the outpatient department, the patient practices many new skills that are generally useful for participating in modern formal organizations, such as keeping track of the days and hours when services are open, forming queues, reading signs, selecting a window or service catering to his classification, communicating with a stranger about a special subject, remembering and following instructions, and taking written orders to another office. Since the inpatient lives in the hospital according to its rules, he learns many other important modern ideas, such as washing, disposal of dirt, diet, and physical care of adults and children.[90]

Since the modern hospital mobilizes equipment and power, the patients and the lower-ranking employees may obtain their first experiences in adjusting to them. The discrepancy between the technological expectations of the Western hospital and the capacities of the personnel and clientele in underdeveloped countries is demonstrated whenever a new building is erected in Asia or Africa. For example, before 1960, the Hadassah Hospital in Jerusalem was housed in makeshift quarters, and medical care and work organization were simple. Suddenly the hospital—and its numerous patients and workers born in the Middle East—was moved into an ultramodern building designed according to the latest American blueprints.[91] The highly mechanized building required speed, work integration, and technical *savoir faire* that the lower employees and patients had never learned during lives spent on primitive farms and in urban slums. For example, the large self-service elevators were frightening and confusing to people who had never before seen them. The automatic opening and closing of doors terrified many; the flow of work throughout the hospital was repeatedly delayed by passengers whose uncertainty about the mechanism led them to push the buttons for all the floors. Communicating from nursing station to bedside by intercoms rather than by face-to-face conversation made many nurses and patients anxious. Maintenance men did not believe the automatic boilers could work reliably by themselves and caused damage and accidents by tinkering. The idea of pushing large wheeled objects through swinging doors was new, and much damage was caused to both objects and doors. Some patients had to be taught that toilets were not drinking wells. Some employees and patients had to be taught to eliminate in the toilets and not in the corners or on the hospital grounds. Some patients had to be taught that a bed is not a tent, that one sleeps on it rather than under it.

Nurses. Besides learning modern techniques of medical care and organizational procedure, the nurses in developing countries learn the personal style of life common to nurses elsewhere. Nursing is one of the best opportunities for rural and poor urban girls in developing countries to rise into the more affluent upper classes. The hospital provides them with comfortable rooms, European meals, and personal amenities. With their money, they buy Western clothing and cosmetics. In speech and deportment, they emulate the indigenous elites and the Western matrons, ward sisters, and nurse tutors who remain in the country. Nursing is a vehicle for modernization in consumption and life style.[92]

The hospital contributes to the general transformation of family structure and sex roles in the social system by altering the position of one group of women. Perhaps in the society traditionally, no woman—and particularly no single woman—gave orders to any man. But in the hospital, female ward sisters must control male patients. At first, the nurses hesitate and the men resist. Ultimately, nurses learn to exercise their authority confidently and tactfully, and the public agrees.[93] As patients, the population encounters women who—as nurses—have learned more scientific knowledge and have more modern skills than they possess. Since they contribute income, exercise authority in the hospital, and marry other members of the modernized elites, nurses conduct their home lives in a more egalitarian fashion than prevails in the less modernized sectors of the society.[94]

Hospitals are modernizing influences because they organize people on universalistic principles. Many preindustrial societies are divided by tribal identity, ethnic groupings, and language. But the hospital recruits its employees not by tribe but by qualifications and—because of shortages of staff—by the mere willingness to work. Employees are assigned throughout the organization according to training and skill. Patients are accepted and distributed not by tribe—except during civil wars that would disrupt the hospital —but by clinical problem. Hospitals are among the first organizations in a society that bring many groups together and give them a chance to interact on common principles.[95] The acquired ability to communicate with and work with different people to perform medical tasks can be generalized as similar universalistic organizations are encountered in the society, such as schools and factories.

The modernization of folk medicine. If populations in developing countries learn about the effectiveness of hospitals' antibiotics and surgical services, the lesson is not lost on folk doctors. In order to keep their clienteles, many modernize their practices by offering the same pills and injections as the hospitals. Many nonmagical folk doctors evolve into general practitioners for the lower classes, offering a combination of traditional and modern methods.[96]

Not only do folk doctors adopt useful methods from Western medicine to accomplish the same cures as their modern-style competitors, but governments help them. Some Asian regimes have created schools where folk doctors can learn a more systematic version of their herbal and other traditional remedies, but where they can also learn many methods from Western general practice.[97] Partly these governments are motivated by the need to meet the chronic deficit of general practitioners in the rural areas and urban slums. Partly the governments are motivated by politics: the nationalist political parties believe the folk doctors can influence many votes in the villages. Probably much of the shortage in general practice will be met by incorporating the nonmagical folk doctors into modernized medical services, like the assimilation of the homeopaths and osteopaths into the medical professions of several Western countries.[98]

Summary

Following are the principal economic variables used in this chapter. Included also are highly correlated variables of a slightly different type that are usually considered indicators of economic development, such as urbanization and literacy.

C.1 National income per capita
C.2 Volume of industry
C.3 Proportion of labor force in industry
C.4 Proportion of population in cities
C.5 Proportion of population with satisfactory literacy

Following are the principal propositions from this chapter. The list of dependent organizational variables appears at the end of Chapter 1.

The poorer the population (C.1) and/or the less literate the population (C.5), then:

The more unequal the utilization of hospitals by class (1.4.2 and particularly 1.5.2)
The later the referral (1.6)
The less exhaustive is diagnosis and treatment (4.12)
The lower the rate of recovery at discharge (6.1)
The higher the rate of relapse after discharge (6.2)
The greater the proportion of surgical cases (6.3)
The wider the discrepancies in providing clinical and nonclinical services (4.1 and 4.2)
The greater the deviation from organizational rules (4.4)
The lower the cohesion between higher and lower ranks (3.7)
The lower the cohesion between employees and patients (4.15)

The greater the volume of industry (C.2) and/or the greater the proportion of the labor force in industry (C.3), then:

The greater the amount and complexity of equipment (1.3)

The greater the number of departments (2.2)

The larger the proportion of technicians in the staff (2.3.5)

The greater the voice of technically trained persons in management (3.2)

The more discretion is granted employees (3.5)

The greater the tendency to treat patients by clinical need rather than according to personal characteristics (4.3)

The higher the rate of innovation in organization and in performance (4.6)

The more complex the work (4.10)

The more thorough the diagnosis and treatment (4.12)

The fewer the interruptions of work because of shortages or malfunctions (4.14)

The larger the proportion of the population in cities (C.4), then:

The more even the distribution of personnel and facilities relative to population (1.7 and 2.3)

The larger the average hospital (2.1)

The earlier the referrals (1.6)

The more literate the population (C.5), then:

The more skilled the employees (1.1.2)

The larger the proportion of graduate nurses and the smaller the proportion of unskilled persons on the staff (2.3.2, 2.3.3, and 2.3.4)

The larger the number of participants in management (3.2)

The greater the discretion given to employees (3.5)

The less coercive the controls (3.6) and the greater the conformity to organizational rules (4.4)

The greater the cohesion among ranks (3.7)

The greater the complexity of work (4.10)

The greater the information given by and received by patients during diagnosis and treatment (4.12)

Notes

1. The incidence of illness by disease and by country is summarized in the numerous publications of the World Health Organization, particularly *First Report on the World Health Situation, 1954–1956* (Geneva: W.H.O., 1959), *Second Report on the World Health Situation* (Geneva: W.H.O., 1963), and the monthly *Epidemiological and Vital Statistics Report*. A detailed treatise describing the clinical problems in preindustrial societies—including comparisons with the illnesses and symptoms of Europeans—is Michael Gelfand, *The Sick African* (Cape Town: Juta, 3rd ed., 1957). For a convenient overview of the differences between developed and underdeveloped countries in health and in medical administration, see Etienne Fournier, *L'Action médico-sociale dans les pays en voie de développement* (Paris: J.-B. Baillière et Fils, 1961). A thorough guide to the administration of hospitals and other medical services in underdeveloped countries is Maurice King (ed.), *Medical Care in Developing Countries* (Nairobi: Oxford University Press, 1966). A good summary of the changes in the population's health and in medical services that accompany economic growth appears in Mark Perlman, "Economic Aspects of the Health Industry in Dynamic Societies," *The American Journal of Public Health*, 53:3 (March 1963), 381–391.

2. Maurice Moyal, "Medicine for the Blue Warriors," *Nursing Mirror*, 108:2802 (16 January 1959), x; Cicely D. Williams, "Social Medicine in Developing Countries," *The Lancet*, April 26, 1958, p. 863; P. J. Whelan, "First Impressions of Medicine in Nigeria," *Journal of the Irish Medical Association*, 44:259 (January 1959), 21–22; Margaret C. Newmark, "Family Doctor in Ibadan," *Medical World*, 97:3 (September 1962), 204; A. L. Thomas and I. D. Thomas, "Medical Impressions of Ghana, West Africa," *The Journal of Medical Education*, 36:6 (June 1961), 699; Benjamin D. Paul (ed.), *Health, Culture and Community: Case Studies of Public Reactions to Health Programs* (New York: Russell Sage Foundation, 1955), passim, especially pp. 112–133; and Ruth F. Woodsmall, *Women and the New East* (Washington: The Middle East Institute, 1960), p. 212.

3. E.g., A. H. Klokke, "Medical Care in the Tropics," *The Lancet*, 17 June 1961, p. 1337; P. J. Whelan, "First Impressions," p. 22; and C. R. M. Prentice, "The Land of the Million Elephants—Two Years with a Medical Team in Laos," *The Lancet*, August 10, 1963, p. 290.

4. Martin Jarrett-Kerr, *African Pulse: Scenes from an African Hospital Window* (London: The Faith Press, 1960), pp. 33–43.

5. For statistics on overcrowding and descriptions of the adverse effects on hospital function and doctors' morale, see John R. McGibony, "Health Care in India: Its Patterns and Problems," *Hospitals*, 35:10 (May 16, 1961), 51–52; John H. L. Cumpston, *Report on the Medical and Public Health Organizations of Ceylon* (Colombo: Ceylon Government Press, 1950), pp. 44 and 55–63 passim; Bennett Hance, *Report on the Organisation of the Health Services of Ceylon* (Colombo: Government Publications Bureau, 1956), pp. 45–46 and 49–52; J. N. Rea, "West

African Journey—Lagos to Ibadan," *Medical World*, 95:6 (December 1961), 65; Naomi Mitchison, "Rising Standards in Nigeria: University College Hospital," *Medical World*, 87:4 (October 1957), 335; Ahmed Kamel Mazen, "Development of the Medical Care Program of the Egyptian Region of the United Arab Republic," (Stanford: unpublished dissertation for the Ph.D. in Medical Care Administration, Stanford University, 1961), pp. 40, 72, and 273–275; Infirmarius, "Hospitals in South Africa," *The Hospital*, 56:5 (May 1960), 361; Infirmarius, "Hospitals in Central Africa," *The Hospital*, 56:10 (October 1960), 841; H. S. Gear, "Some Problems of the Medical Services of the Federation of Rhodesia and Nyasaland," *The British Medical Journal*, August 13, 1960, 528–530; Newmark, "Family Doctor in Ibadan," p. 203; A. W. Williams, "The History of Mulago Hospital and the Makarere College Medical School," *East African Medical Journal*, 29 (July 1952), 258; Kaniz Mowla, "Progress in Pakistan," *The American Journal of Nursing*, 58:2 (February 1958), 238; and C. Mani, "Medical Education in South East Asia," *The Journal of Medical Education*, 37:9 (September 1962), 931.

6. Hilda Hertz Golden, "Literacy and Social Change in Underdeveloped Countries," *Rural Sociology*, 20:1 (March 1955), 4.

7. J. S. Furnivall, *Colonial Policy and Practice* (Cambridge: The University Press, 1948), pp. 359–362; Ahmed Kamel Mazen, "Hospital Administration in Egypt," *Journal of the Ministry of Health* (Cairo), 1:3 (January 1960), 55; Klokke, "Medical Care in the Tropics," pp. 1136–1137; E. A. Beet, "The Daily Life of a Doctor in Kano, Nigeria," *Central African Journal of Medicine*, 3:10 (October 1957), 411–412; Infirmarius, "Hospitals in Central Africa," p. 840; Oscar Lewis, "Medicine and Politics in a Mexican Village," in Paul (ed.), *Health, Culture, and Community*, Ch. 15; J. N. Rea, "Medicine in Ghana," *Medical World*, 96:1 (January 1962), 66; John M. C. Bisset, "Medical Practice in the Land of Anna and the King," *The Practitioner*, 187 (July 1961); George M. Foster, *Problems in Intercultural Health Programs* (New York: Social Science Research Council, 1958), p. 25; and Nancie Solien Gonzalez, "Health Behavior in Cross-Cultural Perspective: A Guatemalan Example," *Human Organization*, 25:2 (Summer 1966), 123–124.

8. On caste differences in utilization of Western and folk doctors in India, see Harold A. Gould, "The Implications of Technical Change for Folk and Scientific Medicine," *American Anthropologist*, 59:3 (June 1957), 511–513; on the differences among religious denominations, see Cicely D. Williams and J. W. Scharff, *An Experiment in Health Work in Trengganu, Malaya* (Beirut: School of Public Health, American University, 1960), p. 18.

9. Janet Welch, *Nursing Related to the Cultural Background in East and Southeast African Colonies* (New York: King's Crown Press, 1941), p. 29; Newmark, "Family Doctor in Ibadan," p. 204; Robert C. Stever, "Medical Impressions from India and Nepal," *The Journal of Medical Education*, 36:4 (April 1961), 335–336; F. J. Bennett, "The Use of Services by Newcomers to the Towns of East Africa," *The Journal of Tropical Pediatrics*, 12:3 Suppl. (December 1966), 66–67; and D. B. Jelliffe, "The Organisation of MCH Services in Developing Regions: Hospital Services for Children, *The Journal of Pediatrics*, 13:1 (March 1967), 40.

10. Grantly Dick Read, *No Time for Fear* (London:Heinemann, 1955), pp. 156 and 191.

11. The great range in the number of maternity beds generally and in the number of special maternity hospitals in countries of similar economic level can be inferred from *World Health Statistics Annual 1962* (Geneva: World Health Organization, 1966), Vol. III, pp. 138–182.

12. Stever, "Medical Impressions from India and Nepal," p. 335; Williams and Scharff, *Experiment in Health Work*, pp. 18, 32, and 34; and Robert F. L. Logan, "International Studies of Illness and Health Services," *The Milbank Memorial Fund Quarterly*, 46:2, Part 2 (April 1968), 137–138.

13. Cicely D. Williams, "Social Medicine," pp. 921–922.

14. E.g., J. A. Curran and N. L. Gault, "Korean Medical Education," *The Journal of Medical Education*, 37:9 (September 1962), 942.

15. E.g., Myron E. Wegman, "Pediatric Education Around the World," *The Journal of Medical Education*, 36:1 (January 1961), 38; and King (ed.), *Medical Care in Developing Countries*, Ch. 13.

16. S. Z. Levine, "Pediatric Education at the Crossroads," *American Journal of Diseases of Children*, 100:5 (November 1960), 39–44. New thinking in pediatrics emphasizes preventive medicine, social and emotional guidance, and other tasks performed with ambulatory patients outside the hospital, e.g., W. S. Craig, "Changing Emphases in Pediatrics: The Challenge of Our Times," *Acta Medica Scientiarum Hungaricae*, 15:1–4 (1960), 65–77.

17. Sources: Ahmed Kamel Mazen, "Development of the Medical Care Program," p. 104; Bisset, "Medical Practice in the Land of Anna and the King," p. 74; *The Health Services of Tanganyika: A Report to the Government by the African Medical and Research Foundation* (London: Pitman Medical Publishing Company, 1964); Agerico Sison, "Medical Education in the Philippines" (Manila: unpublished television speech, 2 December 1960), p. 6; *Public Health Service in Stockholm* (Stockholm: Stockholms Stads Sjukvardsstyrelse, 1960), pp. 3 and 5; and Alain Laugier and C. Besson, "L'Espace médical français," *Le concours médical*, 83:23 (10 June 1961), 3355–3362. Urban–rural imbalances for other countries are reported in George A. Wolf, "Medical Education in Tehran, Iran," *Journal of Medical Education*, 34:10 (October 1959), 1043; D. F. McCarthy, "Afghan Interlude," *Journal of the Irish Medical Association*, 36:212 (February 1955), 30; I. S. Falk, "Medical Care in Two Areas of Southeast Asia—Malaya and Singapore," *American Journal of Public Health*, 48:4 (April 1958), 449–450; I. S. Falk, *Health in Panama: A Survey and a Program* (Stonington, Conn.: Privately printed, 1957), p. 103; I. S. Falk, *Report on the Social Insurance Program in Haiti* (Washington: Federal Security Agency, 1951), pp. 41–44; Benjamin Viel, "Relationship Between the Number of Doctors per Inhabitant and the Economic Development of Latin America," *The Journal of Medical Education*, 34:8 (August 1959), 733; Jose M. Ugarte, "Los medicos como recursos de Salud," *Cuadernos Medico-Sociales*, 4:4

(December 1963), 34; Ragip Uner and Nusret Fisek, *Saglik Hizmetlerinin Sosyalleştirilmesi* (Ankara: T. C. Saglik ve Sosyal Yardim Bakanligi Yayinlarindan, 1961), pp. 144–146; H. S. Halevi, "The Demography of the Israel Physicians," *Hebrew Medical Journal*, 1 (1959), 198–199; and F. J. Bennett et al., "Medical Manpower in East Africa," *East African Medical Journal*, 42:4 (April 1965), 149–161.

18. My computations from Norbottens Läns Landsting, *Sjukvardsinrättningar och barnhem den 31/12 1959* (Lulea: Lanstryckeriet, 1960) and Norbottens Läns Landsting, *Bokslut Statistiska Uppgiffter Framställningar Protokoll* (Lulea: Lanstryckeriet, 1961), pp. 14–15.

19. E.g., Thomas and Thomas, "Medical Impressions of Ghana," pp. 700–701; Stever, "Medical Impressions from India and Nepal," pp. 330–331; James Kennedy, "Bygones of a Bundu Bone Thrower," *The Central African Journal of Medicine*, 3:6, 7, and 8 (June, July, and August 1957), 235–240, 272–274, 315–323; King, *Medical Care in Developing Countries*, Sec. 1:3.

20. Correspondent, "Health Services in Italy," *Medical World*, 96:6 (June 1962), 518–522.

21. Their motives and methods are described in Vladimir Ponedelnik, "Obshiestvennaya profiesseia," *Izvestia*, July 6, 1960, p. 5; and G. Kurzhiiamskii, "Vrach opustil selo," *Meditsinskii Rabotnik*, No. 103, 1961, p. 2.

22. Uner and Fisek, *Saglik Hizmetlerinin Sosyalleş tirilmesi*, pp. 144–148 compared with *Türkiye'de Mevcut Bilcümle Saglik Müesseselerinin Isimlerini ve Yatak Sayilarini Gösterir Liste* (Ankara: T. C. Sihhat ve Ictimai Muavenet Vekâleti, 1959).

23. Complete statistics can be found in *World Health Statistics Annual 1962* (Geneva: World Health Organization, 1966), Vol. III, pp. 120–137.

24. *Report of the Ministry of Health for the Year Ended 31st December, 1960* (London: H. M. S. O., 1961), Part I, p. 190.

25. Uner and Fisek, *Saglik Hizmetlerinin Sosyalleş tirilmesi*, p. 161.

26. World Health Organization, *Annual Epidemiological and Vital Statistics, 1959* (Geneva: W.H.O., 1962), pp. 690 and 692.

27. *World Health Statistics Annual 1962* (Geneva: W.H.O., 1966), Vol. III, pp. 96–108.

28. *Report of the Ministry of Health for the Year Ended 31st December 1960*, Part I, p. 190.

29. For example, compare the statistics for Turkey and for Holland, the latter published in "Overzicht van de Gegevens der Ziekenhuizen in Nederland over de Jaren 1958 en 1959," *Verslagen en Mededelingen Betreffende de Volksgezondheid*, No. 9, September 1961, pp. 810–817.

30. Comparative nurse–bed ratios may be computed easily from *World Health Statistics Annual 1962* (Geneva: W.H.O., 1966), Vol. III, pp. 68–93 and 138–178.

31. My computations from Norbottens Läns Landsting, *Sjukvardsinrättningar och barnhem den 31/12 1959* and Norbottens Läns Landsting, *Bokslut Statistiska Uppgiffter Framställningar Protokoll*, pp. 14–15.

32. Uner and Fisek, *Saglik Hizmetlerinin Sosyalleş tirilmesi*, pp. 145–146, and *Türkiye'de Mevcut Bilcümle Saglik Müesseselerinin Isimlerini ve Yatak Sayilarini Gösterir Liste.*

33. Agnes W. Chagas, "Trends in Nursing in the Region of the Americas," *International Nursing Review*, 5:2 (April 1958), 21. For this reason, many Latin American governments still rely heavily on nursing nuns. Arthur J. Rubel, "Social Science and Health Research in Latin America," *The Milbank Memorial Fund Quarterly*, 46:2, Part 2 (April 1968), 27–28.

34. Helena F. Reimer, "The Role of Women and the Development of Nursing in Modern Egypt" (Chicago: unpublished thesis for the M.A. in the Social Sciences, University of Chicago, 1957), pp. 1, 53–54, 70, and 74; and Ahmed Kamel Mazen, "Development of the Medical Care Program," p. 315.

35. E.g., Reginald E. Rewell, "Medicine in the New India," *The Lancet*, 13 September 1958, p. 576. The problems of managing hospitals with such highly pyramidal gradients of skill are described in King, *Medical Care in Developing Countries*, Sec. 8:3.

36. E.g., Paul Appleby, *Public Administration in India—Report of a Survey* (Delhi: Manager of Publications, 1953), p. 5; and Albert Waterston, "Administrative Obstacles to Planning," *Economia Latinomericana*, 1:3 (July 1964), 310–311.

37. Miles C. Hardie, "Development in Bahrain," *The Hospital*, 54:4 (April 1958), 256.

38. Eugene P. Campbell et al., "Coordination of Small Hospitals and Community Health Centers," *Revista do Servicio Especial de Saude Publica* (Rio de Janeiro), 6:2 (1954), 544.

39. Talcott Parsons, *The Social System* (New York: The Free Press, 1951), Ch. 10.

40. Alex Inkeles and Peter H. Rossi, "National Comparisons of Occupational Prestige," *The American Journal of Sociology*, 61:4 (January 1956), 329–339; Edward A. Tiryakian, "The Prestige Evaluation of Occupations in an Underdeveloped Country: The Philippines," *The American Journal of Sociology*, 63:4 (January 1958), 390–399; R. Murray Thomas, "Reinspecting a Structural Position on Occupational Prestige, *The American Journal of Sociology*, 57:5 (March 1962), 561–565; Simon Biesheuvel, "Mind, Manners and Morals—Some Problems in Cultural Readjustment," *International Nursing Review*, 3:1 (May 1956), 68; and Georges Balandier, *Sociologie des Brazzavilles Noirs* (Paris: Librairie Armand Colin, 1955), p. 158.

41. E.g., Vera Rubin, "Aspirations and Employment in a Developing Society—Trinidad" (New York: unpublished paper presented to the Seminar on Population

and Social Change, Columbia University, 1962), pp. 8–9.

42. Willy de Craemer and Renée C. Fox, *The Emerging Physician: A Sociological Approach to the Development of a Congolese Medical Profession* (Stanford: Hoover Institution on War, Revolution and Peace, 1968), pp. 63, 69, and 79; G. M. Bull, "Impressions of a Medical Tour of the Eastern and Western Regions of Nigeria," *West African Medical Journal*, 9:4 (1960), 141–142; Thomas and Thomas, "Medical Impressions of Ghana," pp. 695–697; Samson Nathan Mwathi, "Medical Problems in Kenya," *Journal of the National Medical Association*, 52:3 (May 1960), 179–181; Robert S. Morison, "Medical Overseasmanship—Obligations, Oppportunities, Operations," *The Journal of Medical Education*, 36:3 (March 1961), 212; and O. Adeniyi-Jones, "The Problems of General Practice in Africa," *Medical Care*, 2:1 (January–March 1964), 24–25.

43. Talcott Parsons and Renée Fox, "Illness, Therapy and the Modern Urban American Family," *Journal of Social Issues*, 8 (August 1952), 31–44.

44. P. P. Brown, "Learning a Language," *Yearbook of Education* (London: Evans, 1949), pp. 338–341; Paul Fejos, "Magic, Witchcraft and Medical Theory in Primitive Culture," in Iago Galdston (ed.), *Man's Image in Medicine and Anthropology* (New York: International Universities Press, 1963), pp. 50–53 and 58–59; Walsh McDermott et al., "Introducing Modern Medicine in a Navaho Community," *Science*, 131:3396 (29 January 1960), 284; and Karl Deuschle, "Training and Use of Medical Auxiliaries in a Primitive Rural Community" (Geneva: unpublished paper given at Conference on Science and Technology, World Health Organization, 1963). The poetic and inexact Arabic language—so well suited to the Koran—handicaps the Arab intelligentsia in developing several fields of modern knowledge, according to Georges Ketman, "The Egyptian Intelligentsia," in Walter Z. Laqueur (ed.), *The Middle East in Transition* (New York: Praeger, 1958), pp. 483–484.

45. Eria M. Babumba, "An African Patient," *East African Medical Journal*, 31:8 (August 1954), 373–377; Williams, "Social Medicine," pp. 921 and 922; George Foster et al., *Cross-Cultural Anthropological Analysis of a Technical Aid Program* (Washington: Smithsonian Institution, 1951), pp. 130–131; E. A. Barker, "Rural Problems of Paediatrics" in *African Culture and Its Relation to the Training of African Nurses* (Johannesburg: Transvaal Nursing Education Discussion Group, South African Nursing Association, 1954).

46. Margaret Read, *Culture, Health, and Disease* (London: Tavistock Publications, 1966), pp. 116–117; Paul, *Health, Culture, and Community*, pp. 108 and 262–266; Foster et al., *A Cross-Cultural Anthropological Analysis*, pp. 15–16, 29, and 38; and Maurice Orbach, "Visit to Egyptian Hospitals," *The Hospital*, 51 (November 1955), 739–740. Upper class contempt for patients by doctors and patients' distrust of doctors can be found in some of the less developed rural areas of modernized countries too, e.g., Edward C. Banfield, *The Moral Basis of a Backward Society* (New York: The Free Press, 1958), pp. 80–82 and 126.

47. E.g., Paul, *Health, Culture, and Community*, Chs. 4 and 9. In preindustrial societies, the folk doctor who simply purveys medications enjoys less public respect

than the folk doctor who combats hostile spirits. In the former case, it is the medicine rather than the man that has the power to cure. George Way Harley, *Native African Medicine* (Cambridge, Mass.: Harvard University Press, 1941), pp. 13 and 37–38. The Western doctor is considered a purveyor of powerful medications. Galdston believes that the shift from deductive reasoning to inductive methods based on research and evidence has reduced the doctor's mystique and public esteem in modern Europe. Galdston, *Man's Image in Medicine and Anthropology,* pp. 522–523.

48. Infirmarius, "Hospitals in Central Africa," pp. 839, 840; and D. B. Jelliffe and F. J. Bennett, "Indigenous Medical Systems and Child Health," *The Journal of Pediatrics,* 57:2 (August 1960), 253.

49. E.g., George C. Basil, *Test Tubes and Dragon Scales* (Chicago: Winston, 1940), pp. 257–260.

50. Leonard W. Doob, *Becoming More Civilized: A Psychological Exploration* (New Haven: Yale University Press, 1960), pp. 96–97, 149–162, 213–216, and 247; Newmark, "Family Doctor in Ibadan," pp. 203–204; Williams and Scharff, *An Experiment in Health Work,* p. 33; and Foster et al., *A Cross-Cultural Anthropological Analysis,* pp. 27 and 30–31. Comparisons of the advice given by doctors on discharge and the home care that Guatemalan peasants consider reasonable appear in Gonzalez, "Health Behavior," p. 124.

51. Thomas and Thomas, "Medical Impressions of Ghana," p. 699.

52. Gelfand, *The Sick African* ; Whelan, "First Impressions," pp. 21–22; Beet, "Daily Life of a Doctor in Kano," p. 412; Rea, "West African Journey," p. 525; Bisset, "Medical Practice in the Land of Anna and the King," pp. 74–78; and Stever, "Medical Impressions from India and Nepal," pp. 331–332 and 335–337.

53. "An average obstetrics registrar in a Bantu ward generally manages to perform more craniotomies than the master of the Rotunda." A. G. Oettle, "Methods of Research into Diseases of the Bantu," in *African Culture and Its Relation to the Training of African Nurses.*

54. Leo Kuper, *An African Bourgeoisie* (New Haven: Yale University Press, 1965), pp. 223–224.

55. Milton Roemer, *Medical Care in Latin America* (Washington: Pan American Union, 1963), p. 263.

56. J. C. Carothers, *The African Mind in Health and Disease* (Geneva: W.H.O., 1953), p. 89; and Frederick Harbison and Charles A. Myers, *Education, Manpower, and Economic Growth* (New York: McGraw-Hill, 1964), pp. 51–53. On the defects of the educational systems that produce such results, see Harbison and Myers, *Education, Manpower and Economic Growth,* pp. 54–57 and 78–80. On differentials in work habits and productivity in developed and underdeveloped countries more generally, see Gunnar Myrdal, *Asian Drama* (New York: Pantheon Books, 1968), pp. 1140–1146. Examples are plentiful when comparing industry, as in Lord

W. M. Hailey, *An African Survey* (London: Oxford University Press, rev. ed., 1957), pp. 1393–1398; A. F. A. Husain, *Human and Social Impact of Technological Change in Pakistan* (Dacca: Oxford University Press, 1956), Vol. I, pp. 236–237 and 284–285; and Frederick Harbison and Ibrahim A. Ibrahim, *Human Resources for Egyptian Enterprise* (New York: McGraw-Hill, 1958), pp. 69–70.

57. Frederick Bartlett, *Remembering* (Cambridge: The University Press, 1932), Chs. 14–19 passim.

58. Gideon Sjoberg, *The Preindustrial City* (New York: The Free Press, 1960), pp. 302–304.

59. Analyses of the social experiences and personality traits that prevail in the most underdeveloped countries and that are discontinuous with the needs of Western-style jobs may be found in Simon Biesheuvel, *African Intelligence* (Johannesburg: South African Institute of Race Relations, 1943); Simon Biesheuvel, "The Study of African Ability," *African Studies*, 11:3 (September 1952), 106–110; Simon Biesheuvel, "The Occupational Abilities of Africans," *Optima*, 2 (1952); Simon Biesheuvel, "The Abilities of Africans," in Prudence Smith (ed.), *Africa in Transition* (London: Max Reinhardt, 1958), pp. 30–38; J. D. Carothers, "Frontal Lobe Function and the African," *The Journal of Mental Science*, 97:406 (January 1951), 25–32; Carothers, *The African Mind*, pp. 85–94 and 108–110; Doob, *Becoming More Civilized*, especially Chs. 6 and 7; Bert Hoselitz et al., *The Progress of Underdeveloped Areas* (Chicago: The University of Chicago Press, 1952), Part II; and Wilbert E. Moore, *Industrialization and Labor: Social Aspects of Economic Development* (Ithaca: Cornell University Press, 1951). For descriptions of the personal adjustment problems resulting for student nurses, staff nurses, and auxiliaries, see *African Culture and Its Relation to the Training of African Nurses*; Welch, *Nursing Related to Cultural Background*, pp. 7 and 25; Hilary James, "African Nurse," *Nursing Times*, 58:41 (October 12, 1962), 1295–1296; and Petersen, "African Nurse Training," p. 330.

60. Thomas and Thomas, "Medical Impressions of Ghana," pp. 698–699; Orbach, "Visit to Egyptian Hospitals," pp. 740–742; and Jane C. Wright, "A Survey of Medical Conditions in Ghana in 1957," *Journal of the National Medical Association*, 53:4 (July 1961), 315.

61. Henry C. Burdett, *Hospitals and Asylums of the World* (London: J. & A. Churchill, 1893), Vol. III, pp. 579–581 and 642–643. On the unsanitary and chaotic conditions in the outpatient departments and wards of London hospitals just before the invention of sterile technique and other modern methods, see Frederick Treves, *The Elephant Man, and Other Reminiscences* (London: Cassell, 1923), Ch. II.

62. Robert S. Myers, "Quality of Patient Care—Measurable or Immeasurable," *The Journal of Medical Education*, 36:7 (July 1961), 777.

63. Hilary James, "African Nurse," p. 1296.

64. A. B. Taylor, "The Impact of Christianity on African Culture in Its Relation to the Training of African Nurses," in *African Culture and Its Relation to the*

Training of African Nurses..

65. B. Lyon, "With the Friends Service Unit in Korea," *Nursing Mirror*, 108 (November 14, 1958), xv; M. A. Cormack, "Posing the Problem," and M. Brandel, "Assessment of Value of Study Course," in *African Culture and Its Relation to the Training of African Nurses*.

66. Pauline Estelle King, "Potential Use of Nurses in Primary Health Centers in Madras State, India" (New York: unpublished dissertation for the Ed.D. in Nursing Education, Columbia University, 1962), Ch. 6, pp. 11 and 16–17; and Leo Kuper, *African Bourgeoisie*, pp. 224–225.

67. Taylor, "Impact of Christianity."

68. E.g., Frank M. LeBar and Adrienne Suddard (eds.), *Laos: Its People, Its Society, Its Culture* (New Haven: HRAF Press, 1960), p. 186; and C. Fraser Brockington, "Public Health in Siam," *Public Health*, 72:5 (August 1958), 166–167.

69. E. W. Petersen, introductory remarks, in *African Culture and Its Relation to the Training of African Nurses*.

70. Sjoberg, *The Preindustrial City*, p. 92.

71. E. R. Foster, "Problems Faced by Ward and Theatre Sisters When Training African Nurses" and Taylor, "The Impact of Christianity," in *African Culture and Its Relation to the Training of African Nurses*.

72. Photographs and descriptions of old Paris hospitals still in use appear in *Cent Ans d'Assistance Publique à Paris* (Paris: Administration Générale de l'Assistance Publique à Paris, 1949). Some of the ancient European hospital buildings are historical and artistic monuments protected by Ministries of Culture, and hospital administrators cannot alter the building at will in order to serve the engineering and organizational needs of modern medical care, e.g., *Siena R.R. Spedali Riuniti di S. Maria della Scala* (Milan: Luigi Alfieri, n.d.).

73. Williams, "Social Medicine," p. 864.

74. John McFie, "With W.H.O. in the Congo," *The Lancet*, March 11, 1961, pp. 550–551; and Rea, "Medicine in Ghana," p. 66.

75. E.g., Ivan D. London, "Instrumentation in Soviet Psychological Research," *The Journal of Social Psychology*, 52 (1960), 51–65 passim; McCarthy, "Afghan Interlude," p. 31; Reimer, "The Role of Women," p. 40; and Bennett Hance, *Report on the Organisation of the Health Services of Ceylon* (Colombo: Government Publications Bureau, 1956), pp. 8 and 36. On the weak motives to maintain facilities throughout the economies of underdeveloped countries, see Albert O. Hirschmann, *The Strategy of Economic Development* (New Haven: Yale University Press, 1958), Ch. 8. Hirschmann's proposed remedy—the adoption of continuous process technology that will dramatize breakdowns and will generate early demands for maintenance—is not possible in most areas of hospital work.

76. E.g., Ray E. Trussell et al., *Medical and Hospital Care in Puerto Rico* (New

York: School of Public Health and Administrative Medicine, Columbia University, 1962), Ch. 3, passim.

77. Rea, "Medicine in Ghana," p. 66; Stephen J. Askin, "Medical Experience in Thailand," *The New Physician*, 11:2 (May 1962), 147–148; Jane C. Wright, "Survey," pp. 314 and 315; and Trussell et al., *Puerto Rico*, Ch. 3 passim.

78. E.g., Hance, *Report on Health Services*, p. 8.

79. E.g., Infirmarius, "Hospitals in South Africa," p. 360; and Orbach, "Visit to Egyptian Hospitals," p. 739. Thefts were even more common before the introduction of modern administrative controls and a more disciplined nursing service. E.g., Alice Wilkinson, *A Brief History of Nursing in India and Pakistan* (Delhi: The Trained Nurses' Association of India, 1958), p. 9. Advice about discouraging thefts of particular items appears in King, *Medical Care in Developing Countries*, Sec. 8:7. Because thefts result from poverty and alienation, they can occur—but on a less extensive scale—in the most modernized countries afflicted by deep class or racial divisions, e.g., "Hospitals to Add 95 Security Aides," *The New York Times*, November 24, 1965, pp. 1 and 29. On the problems of corruption in underdeveloped countries more generally, see Myrdal, *Asian Drama*, Ch. 20.

80. Reinhard Bendix, *Work and Authority in Industry* (New York: Harper & Row, 1963), pp. 10–11.

81. Centralization at the top occurs in other organizations in societies with low education and low literacy, e.g., Richard N. Farmer and Barry M. Richman, *Comparative Management and Economic Progress* (Homewood, Ill.: Richard D. Irwin, 1965), Ch. 6.

82. Dana W. Atchley, "The Changing Physician," *The Atlantic Monthly*, August 1956, pp. 29–31.

83. E.g., the trend in American hospitals, described by Robert N. Wilson, "The Physician's Changing Hospital Role," *Human Organization*, 18:4 (Winter 1959–1960), 177–183; and Alphonse Dochez, "President's Address" *Transactions of the American Clinical and Climatological Association*, 54 (1938), xix–xxiv.

84. The unlimited nature of medical goals inspired both the contents and the title of René Dubos, *The Mirage of Health* (New York: Harper & Row, 1959). For summaries of malfunctions and complaints even in the richest and most industrialized countries, see Martin E. Segal, "The High Cost of Hospitals," *The Public Interest*, 1:2 (Winter 1966), 39–54; Max Kibler, "The Sick Hospital: Symptoms, History, Findings, and Proposals for Treatment," *Medical Care*, 2:1 (January–March 1964), 54–61; "'Charter' for Hospital Doctors," *British Medical Journal Supplement*, October 29, 1966, pp. 171–174; and Edwin P. Hoyt, *Condition Critical: Our Hospital Crisis* (New York: Holt, Rinehart & Winston, 1966).

85. *Migration of Health Personnel, Scientists and Engineers from Latin America* (Washington: Pan American Health Organization, 1966), Chs. 4 and 5; Ehsan Naraghi, *Formation et utilisation des cadres scientifiques et techniques dans les*

pays d'Amérique Latine, d'Afrique Noire et du Moyen Orient (New York: United Nations Special Fund, 1966); "Heavy 'Brain Drain' Is Worrying Indians," *The New York Times*, April 25, 1967, pp. 1 and 24; and *The Brain Drain into the United States of Scientists, Engineers, and Physicians* (Washington: U.S. Government Printing Office, 1967). Many countries with few doctors of their own depend heavily on expatriates from Europe. But the expatriates' high turnover unstabilizes medical services. For example, Bennett et al., "Medical Manpower in East Africa," 153–154.

86. Many reports of such consultants have been written and some have been published, e.g., *The Health Services of Tanganyika*; and Roemer, *Medical Care*.

87. The failure of Western individualized therapy to meet the medical needs of underdeveloped countries is described by Walsh McDermott, "Modern Medicine and the Demographic-Disease Pattern of Overly Traditional Societies: A Technologic Misfit," *The Journal of Medical Education*, 41:9, Part 2 (September 1966), 137–162. For examples of the now common—but frequently ignored—recommendation that developing countries concentrate their spending less exclusively on expensive new hospitals and more widely on a health system with preventive and ambulatory services, see Marcellino G. Candau, "Hospital Organisation in Developing Countries," *World Hospitals*, 1:6 (October 1965), 442–443; Charles Wilcocks, "A Historical Trend in Tropical Medicine," *Transactions of the Royal Society of Tropical Medicine and Hygiene*, 57:6 (November 1963), 403–408; and D. J. Cauchie, "In Search of an African Hospital Concept," *World Hospitals*, 2:2 (April 1966), 166–169. For an example of one government's preoccupation with new hospital buildings and neglect of the preventive facilities that would cope with the society's widespread illness, see Hance, *Report on Health Services*, pp. 35 and 102–104.

88. *Health Education in the U.S.S.R.* (Geneva: W.H.O., 1963).

89. How organizations exercise modernizing influences over preindustrial populations is described by Elihu Katz and S. N. Eisenstadt, "Some Sociological Observations on the Response of Israeli Organizations to New Immigrants," *Administrative Science Quarterly*, 5:1 (June 1960), 123–129; and Alex Inkeles, "The Modernization of Man," in Myron Weiner (ed.), *Modernization* (New York: Basic Books, 1966), pp. 148–150.

90. Some hospitals in underdeveloped countries organize health teaching of patients and their families, e.g., H. Senkatuka, "Health Education in the Paediatric Division of Mulago Hospital," *The Journal of Tropical Pediatrics*, 12:3, Suppl. (December 1966), 35–36.

91. The building is described in "Hadassah Hebrew University Medical Centre in Jerusalem," *DLW-Nachrichten*, No. 22, 1961, pp. 17–28; and "Hadassah Hebrew University Medical Centre, Jerusalem," *International Hospital Federation News Bulletin*, October 1960.

92. Kuper, *African Bourgeoisie*, pp. 216–217 and 227–230; and Jarrett-Kerr,

African Pulse, pp. 64–69.

93. Kuper, *African Bourgeoisie*, p. 224.

94. Changes and the persistence of some traditional practices in the families of South African nurses are described in Jarrett-Kerr, *African Pulse*, Ch. 5.

95. Kuper, *African Bourgeoisie*, pp. 222–223.

96. E.g., Jack Brown, "Some Changes in Mexican Village Curing Practices Induced by Western Medicine," *America Indigena*, 23:2 (April 1963), 92–120; and T. Spens, "Social Aspects of a Health Education Programme in Trans-Volta Togoland" (London: unpublished paper given at the Seminar on Social and Technological Change, Institute of Commonwealth Studies, 1960).

97. Expert Committee on Ayurveda, *Report* (Trivandrum, India: Printed by the S.G.P. at the Government Press, 1965); Ailon Shiloh, "Programming the Integration of Chinese Traditional and Modern Medicine," The Health Education Journal, 26:1 (March 1967), 37–43.

98. Because of their understanding of the causes and relief of some mental illnesses, witch doctors have been incorporated into the organization of one African mental hospital in collaboration with the Western-trained medical staff. T. Adeoye Lambo, "Mental Health in Nigeria," *World Mental Health*, 11:4 (November 1959), 137; and T. Adeoye Lambo, "Mental Health in Africa," *Medical World*, 95:3 (September 1961), 200.

5

Changes in Society and in Hospital Organization

The factual descriptions in this book have pictured both comparative *statics* and *dynamics*. By *statics*, I mean comparisons of the predominant structural attributes in each of a range of societies. Each society is estimated to have a modal value on macroscopic variable X, such as a religious characteristic; each society is thought to have a modal value on hospital variable Y; and arrangement of countries in a series according to ascending values of X is expected to yield a similar rank order of the same countries on hospital variable Y. The propositions at the end of Chapters 2, 3, and 4 follow this form.

Because the propositions refer to relationships between societal characteristics and hospital traits, they should hold true when comparing social environments within as well as between countries. For example, religious or regional economic differences within a heterogeneous society should be associated with the same variations in the characteristics of its hospitals.

Comparisons can be historical as well as cross-sectional and simultaneous. Throughout this book are descriptions of how the organizational characteristics of hospitals have changed as the religious, family, and economic institutions of the larger society shifted. Therefore, any study of the relationships between organizations and their social settings should not neglect the opportunity to suggest possible contributions to theories of social change.

Systematic research about how the larger social system relates to particular classes of organizations would contribute to a better focus in the present burgeoning literature about social change. Much is being published about change in societies as wholes but, on close inspection, these writings often are vague. Relations among sectors of social systems often are mentioned discursively but are rarely spelled out.[1]

Propositions about Inter-sectoral Change

If macrosociology is the study of relationships among the institutions constituting social systems, theories of social change should be sets of propositions about how changes in one sector of society are associated with changes in another sector. Of course, propositions about formal organizations cannot constitute all of a theory of social change, but they can demonstrate how such theories ought to be constructed and can make important contributions to the total body of knowledge.

Some writings about joint and interactive changes between sectors already have been produced. In particular, much has been published about how changes in the family are associated with increases in industrial employment or with migration from rural to urban areas. Propositions about relations between nonmedical institutions and medical organizations belong to the same style of theory.

The propositions at the end of Chapters 2, 3, and 4 were stated there as cross-sectional comparisons of different societies. But most can be rephrased to compare inter-sectoral relations at different times. For example, the first proposition at the end of Chapter 2 stated:

> The more widely practiced in society are religions that teach help to strangers, then the larger the number of persons working in hospitals.

When reworded, a version of this proposition for inclusion in a theory of social change would say:

> As religions teaching help to strangers acquire more following, the number of persons working in hospitals rises.

Such propositions do not predict that both X and Y must rise—for example, religions teaching such doctrines may in fact grow, decline, retain the same following, or fluctuate. But such propositions say that changes in X are associated with particular changes in Y—i.e., when such religions spread, hospital recruitment becomes easier. Thus understood and appropriately worded, perhaps every proposition in our list can refer both to cross-sectional structural comparisons among societies and to changes in one society.

The stages in developing such inter-sectoral propositional theories of social changes are the same as the stages in generating cross-cultural theories. At present, we are beginning to collect data systematically and are offering hypotheses in simple language and with limited empirical support. After considerable empirical research, more abstractly worded propositions will be suggested and verified. Ultimately systems of interrelated propositions about social change can be produced, combining a few broadly applicable variables.

Typological Theories

Another strategy in thinking about social change begins with the construction of types. All societies are classified among a few types, according to a few variables selected as most crucial, according to some theory of social structure. A theory of social change attempts to explain why a society develops from one type to another. In empirical research, one problem is to ascertain how closely each society approximates each theoretical type; another is to determine whether a society moves away from one type toward another in all the dimensions constituting the typology.

Theorizing about the relations between social systems and constituent organizations can involve typological reasoning as well. Types of society can be postulated theoretically and can be located empirically. A particular kind of organization can be examined in all societies (such as hospitals), and types of organization (such as different types of hospital) might be constructed theoretically. The empirical problem then is whether shifts in a society's central tendency from one type to another result in changes in its modal organizational type from the one associated with the antecedent social system to the one associated with the subsequent social system.[2]

One method of classifying societies is by polar positions on a single central variable, such as degree of differentiation (or "functional specificity") in its institutions and social relations.[3] One could then speculate and analyze empirically how hospitals change as a society becomes more or less differentiated. Further, one might construct theoretically various types of hospitals and either deduce logically or establish empirically that each type of hospital corresponds to a particular type of society.

A simple one-dimensional classification of societies is possible in studying comparative statics and change in medical organization, but that is too simple. Religion, the family, and the economy vary independently enough that the best typology should be multidimensional. A great number of typologies can be suggested, according to the taste and purposes of the theorist. Table 2 suggests some elements from this book that might be included in typologies concerning societies and hospitals.[4]

The table is a condensed[5] summary of how clusters of institutional characteristics seem associated with various types of hospital. The bases for four typologies are suggested. The first column offers four ways of classifying hospitals. In the three other columns, each line represents one way of characterizing a society, based on its religious, family, and economic institutions. Judging from my data, a society whose central tendencies fit each cluster of institutional characteristics tend to have the corresponding type of hospital—i.e., each line in the three right-hand columns corresponds to a line in the left column, within each of the four typologies. For example, with respect to a typology concerning "approach to patient," a society probably will have predominantly custodial general hospitals if its social system is characterized by realistic but fatalistic religion and thought, either a nuclear or extended family system, either a predominantly urban or agrarian population, and a commercial-trading economy. But a society with supernatural and activist religion and thought, a nuclear family system, an urban population, and a commercial-trading economy will probably have general hospitals emphasizing spiritual therapy.

TABLE 2
Association Between Types of Hospital and Types of Society

Type of hospital	Types of institutions in the society		
	Religion and prevailing thought	Family	Economy
1. Existence of hospitals			
None	Supernatural or realist, fatalist	Extended	Agrarian, distributive
Some	Supernatural or realist, activist	Any	Agrarian, trade
Many	Realist, activist	Any	Urban, trade or industrial
2. Approach to patient			
Custodial	Realist, fatalist	Any	Urban or agrarian, trade
Therapeutic, spiritual emphasis	Supernatural, activist	Nuclear	Urban, trade
Therapeutic, clinical emphasis	Realist, activist	Nuclear	Urban, industrial
3. Staffing and work methods			
Charitable or apostolic	Supernatural, activist	Any, but usually nuclear	Any, but usually urban and trade
Impersonal and rational	Realist, activist	Nuclear	Urban, industrial
Participation by patient's family	Realist or supernatural, activist	Extended	Agrarian or urban, trade
4. Clientele of each hospital			
Universal	Humanitarian, homogeneous	Nuclear	Egalitarian
Particular groups	Exclusive, diverse	Any, but usually extended	Stratified

Table 2 merely presents some introductory ways of constructing typologies by inference from research. Ideally, graphic names for each type of society should replace multidimensional charts. A theory of social change would hypothesize that movements from one type to another—i.e., downward movements within each enclosed rectangle in the institutional columns of Table 2—should be associated with corresponding downward shifts from one type of hospital system to another.

Historical Evolution: Convergence or Persisting Differentials in Medical Organization

Once much of the literature about social change was addressed to its direction. Generalizations were attempted about whether all societies changed according to a common pattern—unilinear, cyclical, exponential, and so on—and whether all were moving toward the same goal.

Such theories of history have become unfashionable, with one important exception. The present interest in industrialization and modernization has produced speculation about whether industrialization makes societies more similar and whether they will become identical in essentials. At first, several scholars emphasized the increasing convergence; none categorically stated that industrialization ultimately would make all societies alike, but critics suggested this was the logic of the argument.[6] Then a rival literature developed, emphasizing the continued differences among modernized societies.[7]

Much of the debate has consisted of essays written in general language, without much precise evidence. We need detailed studies of how different sectors of societies develop comparatively in several countries. Comparative organizational sociology can make important contributions by specifying whether organizations in some institutional sectors (such as economic) become more alike across societies, whether organizations in other sectors (such as medical) remain essentially different across societies, precisely where the similarities and differences fall, the correlates of these similarities and differences across societies, and the sequence of changes across the entire range of organizations in different institutional sectors within each society.

Since the convergence hypothesis assumes that industrialization is the driving force, it should predict that factory organizations become alike. If developed countries have fundamentally different types of factories—controlling, of course, for size, product, and technology—then the hypothesis is false. That factory organizations throughout the world are becoming essentially identical—as production systems, as social structures, and as psychological environments—has been argued by several authorities.[8] At first sight, this seems plausible. If similar equipment is used to produce similar output, we would expect the organization of work—i.e., the starting point in the social structuring of an organization—to be much alike, regardless of society. The attitudes and behavior of managers and workers might be similar across societies, because of selective recruitment, matching constraints arising from the structure of production, and parallel social experiences.

However, evidence is needed before we can determine whether all social sectors of technically comparable factories ultimately become alike in all countries, and whether the several sectors converge simultaneously. I suspect that even in the most developed countries some sectors of factory structure will remain permanently different, provided that divergences remain in the larger institutions of society that influence these components. For example, authority relations within plants may vary among countries, because of cross-national differences in authority relations throughout society, in trade union systems, in type and role of government, in the labor market, and in the educational system. Even if factories produce the same output with identical equipment, their social organizations may differ because managements by national custom arrange work flows differently or pursue different economic strategies: social relations throughout each plant will vary considerably, depending on whether managements characteristically maximize profits for personal gain, seek to keep the firm stable, or expand.[9]

If factories continue to show differences empirically among the most developed countries today, and if theoretical reasons exist why neither fully modernized countries nor their factories should converge completely, continued differentiation should be even more likely for hospitals. By the nature of their goals and methods of production, hospitals are more variable than factories: hospitals have many more possible goals, they depend on many other institutional sectors for inputs determining both their goals and means, the same ends can be accomplished through various structures, and fewer sectors of the hospital are determined by technology.

Similarities among the world's hospitals arise in some respects from the adoption of similar goals in different societies, the diffusion of medical and organizational techniques across national boundaries, and social feedbacks inducing both the hospital and its suppliers to operate within standardized constraints. Although hospitals were invented spontaneously in many societies in order to house people away from home while undergoing treatment, natural recovery, or terminal illness, most hospitals today originated from the Western type of organization and spread through the efforts of colonial governments, indigenous governments, churches, voluntary associations, and individual doctors. Once established, their utilization eventually increases because news of a few successful treatments spreads, more outpatients and inpatients gain confidence in the hospital, and hospital managements learn how best to please and attract patients. Barriers to referral diminish as feedback occurs within the larger social system of which the hospital is a part: as confidence rises in the hospital's custodial and therapeutic services, the family is willing to transfer to the hospital its own functions in guarding and treating the sick; employers eventually realize that the granting of sick leave is economical, if the hospital restores workers' efficiency.

As in the factory, the technical departments of the hospital reveal considerable cross-national convergence during modernization. The international clinical literature and postgraduate education abroad acquaint doctors with the new equipment and chemicals that cure illness in the most developed countries. At first, the hospital in the less modernized countries assimilates the new technology imperfectly: the buildings, water pipes, and electrical wiring often are ill suited to the new installations; reliable technicians are not produced in sufficient number by the schools; the economy cannot produce additional equipment or a reliable flow of parts; administrators lack experience in controlling the larger number of departments and people that accompany the new equipment. Negative feedback within the hospital touches off negative feedback in the larger society: the medical staffs, hospital administrators, and interested members of the public complain about breakdowns in care, press the schools to give more technical and practical training, urge the government and voluntary associations to invest more money in equipment and in technical staffing, and to press the government to allow more imports and more training abroad. As a result, the physical appearance of hospitals and the social organization of technical services converge throughout the world.

However, the convergence in technical services is not as rapid and perhaps may never be as complete as in the factories of the same range of countries. Industry requires a particular work pace because of the movements of the machinery and the need to cover costs by a minimum output, and factories producing the same output with comparable means have a limited variation in work organization and authority structure. But medical work gives people greater control over their own rate of work, and employment by governments and by charitable associations enables the employees to deviate from international standards of work pace and organization.

Another source of cross-national differences in the technical services of hospitals is medical theory. The accomplishments of scientific Western medicine have led to the abandonment of many medical theories in the West and elsewhere, but Western technical services do not enjoy monopolies everywhere. Ayurvedic medicine, herbal medicine, acupuncture, and certain other methods continue to enjoy the confidence of the public and of governments in many countries, and they have new laboratories and technicians. Western and non-Western staffs coexist—often uneasily—in the technical services of many Asian hospitals. If non-Western medicine suffers little negative feedback or if Western medicine suffers too much of it in these disease-racked societies, hospital organizations may differ from those abroad for some time because of unlike medical practices.

Hospitals differ from factories in their dependence on more nontechnological variables, which slow the pace of convergence. An organization with a fixed goal and a predetermined technology —like a factory producing a particular object in sufficient numbers to cover costs—has a limited range of possible social structures and processes. But hospitals everywhere belong to that class of organizations with ambiguous goals and hence diverse possible social organizations.[10] Unanimous agreement does not exist concerning: when cures are achieved and when the hospital's work ends; whether social-emotional help should accompany physical treatment; whether the patient should retain close ties with family and church during hospitalization; and whether low or high priority should be given to the hospital's insatiable claims on society's resources. Since much of medical care includes the relief of anxiety and the provision of acceptable explanations, folk practitioners often can accomplish as much as scientific doctors in the treatment of chronic nonincapacitating disease, and some societies may give them a permanent place in their community medicine and hospitals.[11]

The ambiguity and variety of goals lead to disagreements within hospitals, differences among hospitals in the same societies, and variations in organization among countries that are otherwise comparable. For example, at present the family participates in treatments in Japan, has liberal visiting hours but no organizational tasks in the United States, has limited visiting hours in Great Britain, and visits adult patients little in the Soviet Union. Religious nursing orders are thought to have no place in most public hospitals in France but continue to work in equally Catholic and equally developed Belgium and Northern Italy. Incorporated into the organization, these nonclinical participants can induce hospitals to pursue their nonclinical goals more emphatically. Such additional subsystems—particularly those belonging also to churches and other nonmedical sectors—complicate the internal unity of hospital organizations.

As societies modernize, increasing differentiation and greater division of labor are accompanied by integration mechanisms.[12] But because they are so sensitive to religious and family institutions that show persisting cross-national variations despite industrial modernization, the hospitals are coordinated in varied ways. In countries where hospitals are nationalized, some regional groupings are created by governments, and a division of labor is established among organizations. But since integration depends on the fiscal strength and priorities of government, and since governments perform differently, hospital networks display a considerable range in integration and economy of management.[13] Whether governments integrate hospitals efficiently with other social institutions that supply important inputs, such as the schools, also varies widely among modernized countries according to the governments' energies and priorities. In some modern countries, hospitals are still owned by voluntary associations connected with the still-powerful Churches. Although the Churches and their associations have become secularized in many respects, their hospitals nevertheless support religious as well as clinical goals, the associations integrate the hospitals among each other and with other social institutions, and the government and interdenominational committees must perform the complex task of integrating separate and often duplicating denominational networks. The professional associations of hospital doctors and nurses are so involved in hospital affairs in some countries that they promote coordination among their organizations; but in many comparable countries, they are no more than scientific societies, or some even hinder coordination of hospital organizations by acting as bargaining agents on behalf of the economic interest of their members.

Every hospital recruits its ranks from different social groups and therefore is a mosaic from that country's ethnic, racial, and class structure. Since modernizing experiences do not affect all groups simultaneously, hospitals in developing countries differ as organizations from those in modernized countries. Doctors and hospital administrators may have similar skills and expectations throughout the world, but the nurses, auxiliaries, and other subordinates vary considerably in assimilating Western clinical and bureaucratic goals and skills. Adverse performance precipitates change: the doctors and hospital administrators exercise closer supervision and improve training. Disagreements about goals may lead to secularization of the hospitals: doctors and lay graduate nurses force out the religious nursing orders, a trend that accelerates the decline in recruitment. Differences between countries in hospital organization may persist after modernization because their stratification profiles and the experiences of all social groups may never become identical. Certain centuries-old group customs may be followed in ways that affect the hospitals indirectly, even when those employees have adjusted to modern hospital work in most ways.[14]

Career opportunities for women may be so great that the country's hospitals will need be organized on the assumption that nursing service will be permanently understaffed or unskilled. While public hospitals will be completely secularized in most countries, religions teaching charity and apostolic service may retain influence in some societies, their religious orders may have learned modern clinical and organizational techniques thoroughly, these establishments may still have religious employees who have responsibilities both to the hospitals and to the Church, and therefore the hospitals' nonclinical goals may be emphasized more prominently than elsewhere.

In summary, the nature of their goals, technology, and work structure cause certain organizations to be much alike all over the world, almost as soon as they are created. They must be similar, in order to produce the same output with similar means; their staffs behave similarly because of selective recruitment, indoctrination, and the constraints of technology and of technically determined work flows. The biggest difference among countries is whether the social infrastructure enables such organizations to exist at all. If they have been created, these organizations change as the larger social system modernizes, but usually they change less than their social environments. Often they are modernizing influences on other organizations, because they are forerunners. Factories approximate this theoretical pole more closely than do other organizations.

On the other hand, certain other kinds of organization—such as hospitals—can exist in a great variety of forms in many different kinds of society. This is possible because they are highly variable in their goals, technology, personnel requirements, and work requirements. These organizations change considerably as changes occur in the social institutions with which they articulate in acquiring their means and demands. They become alike in those organizational sectors articulated with social institutions that become more alike across countries. But where cross-national differences remain in various social institutions that affect sectors of the organization, these organizations to that extent continue to differ. Exactly how changes in organizational variables relate to changes in larger social systems, and how the sequence of changes varies by type of organization and type of society are central problems for research in comparative organizational sociology.

Conclusion

Whether the problem has been cross-national comparisons or social change, this book has suggested more than it can prove. Ways of thinking have been indicated about social institutions and about the formal organizations that they generate, and lists of propositions have been provided. The generalizations often have outrun the data, and therefore these propositions cannot be called verified laws. But while less common in the present age of empiricism, this is not unprecedented. I am not the first sociologist who has succumbed to the intoxicating opportunity of generalizing about the world.

Obviously, verifying propositions about modal organizational characteristics in many societies requires an immense research effort. A considerable number of countries must be picked, providing a sufficient distribution on the independent macroscopic social variables in one's hypotheses. Within each country one must obtain from existing sources or from new research enough information about the macroscopic variables, such as the religious characteristics discussed in Chapter 2. Because a relationship between social environment and organization might vary according to type of organization—for example, it might hold true for large but not for small hospitals—it must be tested across a considerable range of organizations within each country. In other words, if the hypothesis postulates a relationship between religious origins of hospital personnel and the authority structure of the hospital, the data should be collected from a number of hospitals in each country, matched according to size, type of ownership, structure of medical and nursing staffs, and any other organizational characteristics that might confound a relationship between religion and authority. Any relationship between the over-all characteristics of a country and the structural traits of its organizations must be proved and explained, lest it be merely a statistical coincidence.[15]

In the foreseeable future, the verification of hypotheses in comparative organizational sociology in this style will be gradual. Data at first will be collected in a few countries, where experienced research teams have access to organizations in question, which are not too numerous to tax the project's administrative and financial capacities, and which are not too distant geographically. Comparable facts will be obtained by functionally equivalent research operations. Often the variables and hypotheses will be perfected during the course of the research. More studies will fit together on the same themes, and certain propositions about social determinants and organizational characteristics will seem more plausible.[16] Eventually a few variables and propositions can be fitted together in logical systems.[17]

As comparative organizational sociology develops, we should not be inhibited by the counsels of perfection and hesitate to publish hypotheses because the evidence is too difficult to obtain and has not yet been secured in full. In any science, it is only the routine knowledge that is thoroughly verified. The most important ideas often are tentative, outstripping our data but clearly consistent with what we know so far. A virtue of propositional theories is that they offer our hypotheses in testable and falsifiable form, while also summing up the existing evidence.[18] This book will be vindicated if it can point toward the most fruitful directions in comparative organizational sociology, if its tentative findings remain consistent with the results of future research, and if its conclusions can be superseded by more general propositions in the future.

Notes

1. A convenient summary of this literature is Wilbert E. Moore, *Social Change* (Englewood Cliffs, N.J.: Prentice-Hall, 1963).

2. Typological reasoning has been used to compare government organizations in different societies and to explain changes, in Fred W. Riggs, *Administration in Developing Countries* (Boston: Houghton Mifflin, 1964).

3. This is the organizing theme in *ibid.*, and in Robert M. Marsh, *Comparative Sociology* (New York: Harcourt, Brace & World, 1967).

4. In the most fruitful multidimensional typologies of society for purposes of analyzing relations between societies and hospitals, some characteristics of government should be added to the institutions emphasized in this book.

5. Usually typologies are presented with all boxes resulting from their constituent attributes. Ideally a minimum number of attributes should supply the boxes for arranging all the data under review informatively, and no boxes should be empty. Table 2 is a condensation of such a complete array. The collapsing of the complete system of boxes is necessary because of their number: several dimensions among religious, family, and economic institutions are necessary to classify hospitals meaningfully; and the total number of boxes resulting from cross-tabulation of dichotomies is 2^n, where n = number of attributes. The collapsing is justified also because many of the types of society resulting from the full cross-tabulation of all the attributes are theoretically possible but either do not occur empirically or do not have distinctive hospital systems.

6. The best-known recent sociological works emphasizing convergence are Clark Kerr et al., *Industrialism and Industrial Man* (New York: Oxford University Press, 2nd ed., 1964); and Alex Inkeles, "Industrial Man: The Relation of Status to Experience, Perception, and Value," *The American Journal of Sociology*, 66:1 (July 1960), 1–31. A helpful summary of the conceptual issues in the convergence controversy appears in E. G. Dunning and E. I. Hopper, "Industrialisation and the Problem of Convergence: A Critical Note," *The Sociological Review*, 14:2, New Series (July 1966), 164–168.

7. E.g., Arnold S. Feldman and Wilbert E. Moore, "Industrialization and Industrialism: Convergence and Differentiation," *Transactions of the Fifth World Congress of Sociology* (Louvain: International Sociological Association, 1962), Vol. II, pp. 151–169; John H. Goldthorpe, "Social Stratification in Industrial Society," in Paul Halmos (ed.), *The Development of Industrial Societies: The Sociological Review Monograph No. 8* (Keele: University of Keele, 1964), pp. 97–122; and several specialized studies, such as Zbigniew Brzezinski and Samuel P. Huntington, *Political Power: USA/USSR* (New York: Viking, 1964); and Ralf Dahrendorf, *Society and Democracy in Germany* (Garden City, N.Y.: Doubleday, 1967), especially pp. 44–48.

8. E.g., Richard N. Farmer and Barry M. Richman, *Comparative Management and Economic Progress* (Homewood, Ill.: Irwin, 1965), Ch. 15; and Alex Inkeles, "The Modernization of Man," in Myron Weiner (ed.), *Modernization* (New York: Basic Books, 1966), p. 149.

9. Hypotheses about cross-national differences in the social structures of factories in the most developed countries appear in a forthcoming book by four European research centers and myself. We hope to conduct comparative field research to identify the similarities in factory structure, the cross-national differences, and the institutions in the larger social systems that govern these organizational components.

10. W. Richard Scott, "Some Implications of Organization Theory for Research on Health Services," *The Milbank Memorial Fund Quarterly*, 44:4, Part 2 (October 1966), 39–40.

11. Such possibilities in India and in the Middle East are suggested by Harold

A. Gould, "The Implications of Technical Change for Folk and Scientific Medicine," *American Anthropologist*, 59:3 (June 1957), 507–516; and Ailon Shiloh, "The Interaction Between the Middle Eastern and Western Systems of Medicine," *Social Science and Medicine*, 2 (1968), 241–245.

12. Neil J. Smelser, *The Sociology of Economic Life* (Englewood Cliffs, N.J.: Prentice-Hall, 1963), Ch. 5.

13. Many regional arrangements have been proposed and some have been implemented by governments. Among the recommendations are Expert Committee on Organization of Medical Care, *Role of Hospitals in Programmes of Community Health Protection* (Geneva: W.H.O., 1957); Richard Llewellyn-Davies and H. M. C. Macaulay, *Hospital Planning and Administration* (Geneva: W.H.O., 1966), Ch. 1; and Thomas McKeown, *Medicine in Modern Society* (London: Allen & Unwin, 1965), Parts III and VI. For a description of the lag in effective integration in Great Britain, see Thomas McKeown, "The British National Health Service in Perspective," *Medical Care*, 1:3 (July–September 1963), 167–170.

14. For example, the caste taboos about interaction and the appropriateness of certain "higher" or "lower" tasks contradict the functional requirements of modern organization and are often abandoned, but some of India's caste characteristics and related traditions may persist. They are most likely to be preserved in family life and in other personal spheres, and doubtless hospitals will continue to be affected. See Milton Singer, "The Modernization of Religious Beliefs," in Weiner, *Modernization*, p. 64; and Joseph R. Gusfield, "Tradition and Modernity: Misplaced Polarities in the Study of Social Change," *The American Journal of Sociology*, 72:4 (January 1967), 351–362.

15. For example, if a country has a large Catholic population and large hospital staffs, a proposition can validly relate them only if one has a definite connection with the other. The well-known "ecological" or "aggregative" fallacy is described by Matilda White Riley, "Sources and Types of Sociological Data," in Robert E. L. Faris (ed.), *Handbook of Modern Sociology* (Chicago: Rand McNally, 1964), pp. 1020–1021 and sources cited therein.

16. This is much like the method of "juxtaposition" and "balanced comparison" described in George Z. F. Bereday, *Comparative Method in Education* (New York: Holt, Rinehart & Winston, 1964), pp. 22–28; and Bereday, "Reflections on Comparative Methodology in Education, 1964–1966," *Comparative Education*, 3:3 (June 1967), 171–179.

17. On the arrangement of verified propositions in economical systems, see Hans L. Zetterberg, *On Theory and Verification in Sociology* (Totowa, N.J.: The Bedminster Press, 3rd ed., 1965), pp. 96–100 and Ch. 8. Another good book on the creation and empirical validation of propositions is Arthur L. Stinchcombe, *Constructing Social Theories* (New York: Harcourt, Brace & World, 1968). The use of propositional theory in comparative organizational sociology is described in Glenn D. Paige, *Proposition-Building in the Study of Comparative Administration* (Washington: Comparative Administration Group, American Society for Public Adminis-

tration, 1964).

18. For eloquent statements about how to construct scientific theories by trial and error—and about the necessity for bold speculation that initially outruns the evidence—see Karl R. Popper, *Conjectures and Refutations: The Growth of Scientific Knowledge* (New York: Harper, 1968), pp. 51 and 55–56.

Appendix
The Informants

This book would not have been possible without the assistance of many people in each country. The amount of time and hospitality granted an inquisitive foreigner was extraordinary. Following are the persons who generously gave at least an hour of their time in interviews or in equivalent help by correspondence. Some directed me through their organizations. Some even acted as social hosts and tourist guides, in addition to our professional shoptalk. Many others provided valuable information in shorter conversations, but they are too numerous to list.

England. Brian Abel-Smith, George Braithwaite, John L. Burton, Mary F. Carpenter, Jack H. Carrick, Theodore E. Chester, A. E. Cooper, John Dodd, Dr. Dyce, John R. Ellis, M. R. Forbes, Theodore F. Fox, David Glass, W. P. Gill, Doreen Grand, William E. Hall, Vivien M. Jenkinson, Margaret N. Lee, Hugh L'Etang, Brian McSwiney, Fred Martin, Maurice Orbach, Muriel B. Powell, Gertrude A. Ramsden, Thomas Rimmer, Arthur Seldon, Robert W. Sharpington, H. Marjorie Simpson.

U.S.S.R. George Antonov, Dr. Bailin, V. Butrov, Dr. Brilantova, Mark G. Field, Nikolai I. Grashchenkov, A. V. Ikonnikova, Dr. Leonienko, Ira Lubell, Josef Vasilovich Melnik, Sergei Nechaev, Shaber T. Nikolaievna, Elena Pogisantz, Alexander Shevelyov, Dr. Shivanyenko, Mikhail Sokolowski, Alexander Timofeyevski.

France. Robert Attavi, Louis Justin-Besançon, Jean Bui-Dang-Ha-Doan, Frédéric Choffé, Paul Comet, Pierre A. Debuirre, Guy Forestier, Henry Galant, Jacques Gobinet, Jean Guénézon, François Hoquet, Lucien Jolly, Robert Larmagnac, Alain Laugier, Raymond Lecoq, Sister Margaret of the Congregation of Saint-Vincent-de-Paul, E. Martin, Jane Martin, Paul A. Messerli, Henri

Moraud, Jean-Daniel Reynaud, Lucie Ch. Roques, Jean Vatier.

Germany. Fritz Beske, Bruno Buchholz, Maria Gehrt, Sister Gertrud Kuhncke, Werner W. Lerche, Richard Plönes, Heinz Ritter, Dietrich Rüschemeyer, Rolf Schlögell, Rudolf Schütz, Karl Taprogge, Hildegard Twelsiek, Willy Wernick, Mr. Winter, Gerhard Wolff, Sister Wunibalda of the Sisters of the Sacred Heart.

Netherlands. Johan Beunder, Jan C. J. Burkens, Gerard Dekker, Johan Fokkema, Sophie Hooykaas, Menno Klinkenberg, R. A. de Moor, Cornelus Ouwehand, Duurt K. Rijkels, G. A. de Ruiter, Jan van der Valk, Jacques J. Velthoven, Johan C. M. Hattinga Verschure.

Sweden. Anders Åberg, Gunborg Bergkvist, Gunnar Biörck, Karl-Fredrick Blom, Kamrer K. Carlberg, Ingvar Ekholm, Ellen Fahy, Sten Floderus, Ulla Hagberg, Elsa Häggland, Lennart Hammar, John Henriksson, Carl-Gösta Hesser, Astrid Krokstedt, Ebba Nilsson, Rut Olsen, Bror Rexed, Ursula Rexed, Malcolm Tottie, Sven Ydén, Ulf Zetterblad.

Switzerland. Emile-Ch. Bonard, Jacqueline Demaurex, Marjorie Duvillard, Pierre E. Ferrier, Sister Marguerite Genton, D. Grandchamp, Pierre Jaccard, Eric Martin, Jean Maystre, Alex F. Müller, Anne Marie Paur, Hal M. Wells, Bernard Wissmer, Verena Wüthrich, General Secretariat of the Swiss Medical Institutions (and especially Ulrich Naef).

Italy. Giuseppe Billiena, Gimo Civai, Franz Feliciangeli, Oretta Ferrari, Scattan Germana, Father Antonio Grumelli, Elio Guzzanti, Franco Illuminati, Sister Maria Cecilia of the Daughters of Charity, Sister Martina of the Daughters of Charity, Mario Massani, Innocenzo Moretti, Ignazio Muner, Stefania Nutini, Lucio Nuzzolo, Pietro Omodeo, Luigi Pinelli, Piero Pinna, Vittorio Sabena, Marta Safier, Mimmo Sano, Ugo Siniscalchi, Father Germano Tomaino, Angelo Tomasini, Sergio Vulterini.

Spain. Manuel Alonso Olea, Erna Ruth Berndt, Antonio Bustos Alarcón, Salustiano del Campo Urbano, Gerardo Clavero, Tomás Charlo Dupont, Luis Estella Benudes de Castro, Manuel Jimenez Rueda, Juan Linz, Eduardo Martínez Alonso, Mario de la Mata y de la Barrera-Caro, Francisco Merino Prieto, Mercedes Milà Nolla, Alfonso de la Peña, Fernando Enríquez de Salamanca, Antonio Sanchez Dominguez, Sandra Stanway, Mario Zarapico Romero.

Poland. Jan E. Bielecki, Stanislaus Bylina, Helena Csorba, Wiktor Eychner, Jadwiga Izycka, Ryszard Jachowicz, Marcin Kacprzak, Nonna Lyzwanska, Tomasz Niedek, Feliks Oledzki, Ksawery Rowicki, Bronislaw Saldak, Adam Sarapata, Magdalena Sokolowska, Walerian Strasewiez, Ludwik Zukowski.

Greece. Ilias N. Athanasiades, George K. Baritakis, Marie Cecile Bersch, Athanasios Coccalis, Menelaos Germanos, Sofitis Liaticos, John Nicolacopoulos, A. C. Papaioanou, Paul Pavlides, Andreas Placoudas, Victoria Rozou, Anthony Scouloudis, Gregory D. Skalkeas, Athena Tsitouridou, Constantin Valsamis.

Turkey. Shirley Epir, Ihsan Günalp, Aslan Gündaş, Hüsnü A. İkisnişci, R. Louise McManus, Ekmel Onursal, Omer Ozek, Sabahattin Payzin, Serife Sözeri, Yusuf Tunca, Perihan Velioglu.

Cyprus. Ali Atun, Turkan Aziz, Kaya Bekiroglou, Glafkos Cassoulides, Arax Goerderalian, Takis Hadjilambris, Phoebus C. Hadjioannou, Georgette Houry, Sophoulla Lazaridon, George Marangos, Zemon G. Panos, Fikret Rassim, Christos Savvas, Jeanne Shellish, Dmitri Souliotis, Charalambos Stamatiades, George T. Strickland.

Egypt. Mahmoud Abdel Hamud Attiah, James Boyars, Garbis Chemsian, Irene Cooper, Maria P. Tito de Moraes, Jean W. Dooley, Mohamed Loutfi Dowidar, Nawal El-Saadari, Abdul Rahman El-Sadr, Zoheiv Farid, Rita Hill, Paul Jamison, Albert Khalil, Ahmed Kamel Mazen, Moustapha Ramadan, Said Sabon, Elsie Salmi, Ali H. Shaaban, Fathi A. Soliman, Joan B. Stout, Mohamed Talaat, Grace Zawahry.

Israel. Aaron Antonovsky, Hasia Zaretski Gur-Arie, Tova Yeshurun-Berman, Joseph Ben-David, A. Michael Davies, Fritz Dreyfuss, Peter P. Fleischmann, Judith Steiner-Freud, Shabbetai Ginton, Rafael Gjebin, Sonya Goldner, Eda Grünwald, Haim Sholom Halevi, Ben Zion Harell, Itzhak Kanev, Uri Khassis, Sarah Kossowsky, Pinchas Koren, Moshe Krieger, Kalman J. Mann, Jack Medalie, Baruch Oren, Ely Presser, Bella Schwartz, Moshe Soroka, Joseph Stern, Nelu Strulovici, Havraham Yarom.

Lebanon. Joseph E. Azar, Charles W. Churchill, Said Dajani, Thomas H. Gray, Farid Sami Haddad, Jamal Karen Harfouche, Lucy V. Keverian, Yvonne Khouri, Father Pierre Madet, Ibrahim Salti, Aida K. Cotran Shammas, Wadad Shaya, LaVand Syverson.

World Health Organization. Fawzie S. Bisharah, Simon Btesh, Lyle Creelman, Fernanda Alves Diniz, A. C. Eberwein, Edward Grzegorzewski, C. J. Hackett, Elizabeth Hill, William Hobson, Leo Kaprio, Helen Martikainen, M. Claude Petitpierre, Dorothy Potts, Maria Leite-Ribiero, Gabriel Rifka, T. S. Sze, James M. Vine.

Others. R. A. Amarvi, Virginia Arnold, Frances Beck, Hamish Dickie-Clark, Barbara Darbyshire, Pierrette Daubigeon, Salvador Perez Diaz, Fred Fisher, Ruth Freeman, Craig S. Lichtenwalner, Britta Ohlin, Ananda Shiva Prasad, Marie-Andrée Vacherot, Cicely Williams.

In addition, I am indebted to several persons who arranged for informant interviews or for visits to organizations: Mikhail Bruk, Ministry of Health of the U.S.S.R.; Monique Lepeytre, Ministry of Health (now Ministry of Social Affairs) of France; Alphonse Gardie, Assistance Publique à Paris; Mieczyslaw Juchniewicz, Ministry of Health and Social Welfare of Poland; Vassos P. Vassilopoulos, Ministry of Health of Cyprus; Grace Spacht, Eastern Mediterraneous Regional Office, World Health Organization; Miss D. Maitland, International Hospital Federation.

Name Index

Subject Index